# THE LIVING LABORATORY

# THE LIVING LABORATORY

## 200 Experiments
## for Amateur Biologists

JAMES DONALD WITHERSPOON
REBECCA HUTTO WITHERSPOON

*Illustrated by the Authors*

DOUBLEDAY & COMPANY, INC.
GARDEN CITY, NEW YORK
1960

ACKNOWLEDGMENTS

At the end of each chapter are one or more references
to the works of men who have helped us and who will
help you if you read their wisdom. Reading about and
then examining animals has made this book possible. For
more specific contributions we gratefully thank Mr.
Gordon Wesner, Mr. Frank Fisher, Miss Anna Camp,
Professors W. A. Hiestand, J. E. Wiebers, and A. B.
Burdick at Purdue University, as well as Mr. Kenneth
Bush, his practice teachers and students at West Lafayette High School, Indiana, Mr. John Lazar of Tecumseh
Junior High in Lafayette, and Mr. William Kastrinos of
Glenbard High School in Glen Ellyn, Illinois. We also
thank Mrs. Gordon Wesner for reading and criticizing the
completed manuscript. We are especially indebted to the
teachers of the Midwest Biology Institute who told us
there were no satisfactory experimental laboratory
manuals. This is our answer to your request.

To
Our Parents

# PREFACE

For those who want to know nature, there is no better way than to pry off the lid and look inside. In the following chapters and experiments, you do just that. First you read, to gain knowledge of each biological topic. Then you gather a few commonly available materials from home or school and begin one of the various laboratory or field investigations. In these you operate on mice, follow tracks in the snow, grow worms having two heads, and electrically excite nerves and muscles, to mention but a few. And lest your adventurous appetite remain unfilled, we include many suggestions for further research. Some point to uncharted areas of biology in which lie the real thrills for beginner and professional alike.

This book is written for people who want something different, something challenging. It is not a workbook but a book of exploration and experiences designed for those who seek the unknown. Some of these experiments are simple; some are harder and require care to get accurate results. Take pride in your endeavors and learn these lessons well. There is no room for the second best in the world of science. You have a brilliant, rewarding future on earth and in space, a future well worth the effort which makes it possible.

# CONTENTS

APPENDICES

# Tissues and Embryos

## I

## THE BEGINNING OF LIFE

**Materials.**
1. Chicken eggs incubated for four and eight days
2. Hand lens
3. Watch glass and large beaker or pan
4. Sodium chloride (table salt)
5. Scissors

**Life starts simply.** On the yolk of every fertile chicken egg, there is a pinhead-sized, simple-looking, white spot. If a hen sets on the egg, this spot becomes a very animated baby chick in just three small weeks. Here is a Cinderella-like miracle, a turning of mice into horses, and pumpkins into carriages. The blueprint for life is hidden in the spot. We shall see this blueprint transform into an amazing architecture as our story unfolds.

**Three weeks in an egg.** No matter how an egg is turned, the fertile spot always drifts upward since it is lighter than the yolk. This clearly benefits the unborn *embryo,* which is thereby brought closer to the mother hen's breast. In the beginning the heat brings no startling changes, but before the first day closes, the cells divide and extend and finally a fold appears which is the start of the head. Blood vessels and a beating heart evolve during the second day. The miniature circulatory system gradually expands around the yolk from which it picks up nutrients for the growing embryo.

As the days pass, more and more structures develop. There are skin, bone, brain, nerves, muscle, and all the other body parts, but in Lilliputian dimensions. The embryo begins to look like a chicken, and we recognize this by giving it a new name, the *fetus*. About eight to ten days have now passed since the mother hen started setting.

The unborn chick gets its air supply through 7500 funnel-shaped pores in the shell. Air enters the pores more easily than water vapor can escape them. This protects the delicate bird from death by dehydration. Toward the end of incubation the fetus pokes its beak into the air cell at the blunt end of the egg. You have probably noticed this vacant space while eating the "whites" of hard-boiled eggs. The chick gulps air from here.

When ready to emerge, the fetus pecks at the inside of its shell, feebly at first, but with increasing vigor toward the end. A crack and finally a hole form from which the newborn pushes out into the light of our world. His three weeks of captivity are ended.

**The embryo of man.** Chicken embryos are excellent subjects for study—they are easily obtained from hatcheries and the eggs are simple to open—but we must not forget that the miracle of the chick is often repeated throughout the animal kingdom. Even the human begins as a barely visible fertilized egg, but in this case there is no yolk, white, or hard outer shell. The egg enters the mother's womb, or *uterus* and implants itself in the wall of this living incubator (Fig. 1–1). It divides

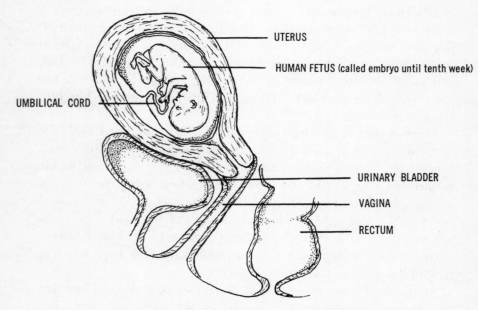

Fig. 1–1. FOUR-MONTH FETUS IN MOTHER'S UTERUS

into two cells and then doubles again and again and again. Soon the little embryo sprouts an umbilical cord containing blood vessels which draw nourishment from the mother's uterus. In time, the heart, liver, brain, and other organs unfold, and finally little buds appear on each side, which will someday become arms, hands, legs, and feet.

The young embryos of all animals bear a marked resemblance to one another. The human is no exception. As a matter of fact, man even grows gills at one stage, as though he might someday become a fish. He also sprouts a small tail, suggestive of other relations, but as time passes the gills, tail, and other odd features are lost till he finally looks like a man. This takes eight to ten weeks. Now he is called a fetus, and he remains a fetus until his birth about seven months later.

**The embryo's "organizer."** What makes seemingly simple, undifferentiated tissue grow into complex organs, arms, and legs? Where do we find the magic brew which brings it about? The answers are not complete but at least a start has been made. By 1918, Hans Spemann, a German embryologist, was able to present his concept of an "organization center." He had operated on the very early embryos of amphibians and removed the blastopore, a region which later becomes the main part of the intestine. This was grafted to another embryo in a different position, but it still developed and, in fact, induced adjacent areas to form a nervous system and backbone. The embryologist thereafter called the blastopore an organizer.

Spemann continued removing and transplanting other structures and found other organizers, many of which were specific for only one organ. For instance, when he took out an eye area, even though it did not remotely resemble an eye at the time, and put it on the flank of another embryo, it developed a lens, a transparent covering, a light receiving area, everything normally present in an eye but nothing else. Of course, an eye on the flank will not see. There are no visual nerves in this region to connect it with the brain.

Spemann transplanted an eye area from a still earlier embryonic stage. This time nothing happened. The eye area blended into the new embryo and had no effect. Age, then, was a factor which decided whether new structures would or would not come forth.

It had been assumed that an organizer was something alive. In 1932, experimenters discovered an exciting contradiction of this idea—the organizer worked even after it had been killed. Apparently some embryo-developer chemical existed within the tissue, dead or alive. Those who attempted to isolate it were surprised to find that many chemicals have an organizing effect, even some which are not found in embryos. They concluded that the secret of embryonic emergence must lie in the reacting tissue itself. It is here that researchers are still concentrating their efforts.

## OPENING AN INCUBATED CHICKEN EGG

Obtain from a hatchery eggs which have been incubated for four and eight days. Prepare a pan or large beaker of water with nine grams of sodium chloride (common table salt) dissolved in one liter of water, or in the English system this would be about two level teaspoons per quart of water. (The metric system, generally preferred by the scientist, is discussed in Appendix A.) Heat the salt solution to 103°F. and maintain it at this temperature throughout the experiment.

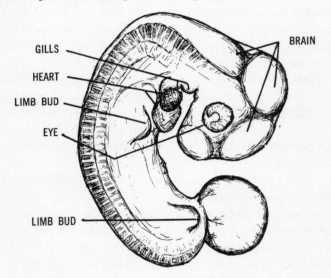

GILLS

HEART

LIMB BUD

EYE

BRAIN

LIMB BUD

### Fig. 1–2 FOUR-DAY CHICK EMBRYO

With the sharp point of scissors, punch a small hole in the eggshell (use a four-day-old chick embryo first) about a third down from one of the ends. Insert the tip of the scissors into this hole and cut carefully around the shell. Hold this egg at the salty water's surface and open it. Let the contents spill gently into the solution, whose salt concentration is approximately the same as that in the egg and, therefore, least harmful to the chick. Rotate the yolk, if necessary, to find the embryo. It will appear as a definitely formed, weirdly arranged, living animal about half an inch long (Fig. 1–2). The size and extent of embryonic development vary somewhat.

**Observing the four-day-old chick embryo.** Look first for a beating heart! With careful work this may continue pumping for several minutes. Cut and pull the embryo free from the yolk. Slide a clean watch glass containing some of the warm salt solution underneath and remove the unborn for closer observation. Use a hand lens for magnification.

Watch the blood as it passes in pulses from the two-chambered heart. Notice the network of blood vessels. The heart later becomes four-chambered, and the vessels develop numerous and important branches. Examine the head end of the embryo. It is expanded to contain the brain. Note the large eyes. Look for *limb buds* at the site of future arms and legs. Look also for gills. These appear as indentations in the neck region between the brain and heart.

Fig. 1–3 EIGHT-DAY CHICK EMBRYO

**Observing the eight-day-old chick embryo.** Remove the embryo from an eight-day egg and transfer it to a watch glass containing salt solution. The appearance now is more like that of an adult chicken (Fig. 1–3). The limb buds are much further developed; probably you will see fingers (later wings) and toes. There is a primitive beak. Look for an ear opening behind the eyes. The bumpy skin, like a plucked hen, shows where feathers will eventually bloom.

## OTHER THINGS TO DO

Fertilized chicken eggs provide a favorite study for embryologists. They can be incubated in semi-humid containers at 37°C. (99°F.) without the presence of meddlesome, brooding mother hens. In some laboratories, plastic windows are added to the shells through which embryonic growth is observed directly. Injection of certain drugs through these windows causes formation of double organs (two hearts, for instance) or complete absence of an organ. Other laboratories grow embryonic tissues indefinitely in appropriate fluids, a sort of short cut to immortality. By these means we obtain clues to normal and defective development of animals before birth.

If you wish to continue experimenting, we suggest that other stages of embryo and fetal development be observed. Although a complicated procedure, tissue sections of embryos may be prepared as described by E. Morholt, P. F. Brandwein, and A. Joseph in their excellent book of experimental procedures, *Teaching High School Science: A Sourcebook for the Biological Sciences,* Harcourt, Brace and Company, New York, 1958. Older fetuses can be dissected for the study of specific organs.

# MICROSCOPES AND ANIMAL TISSUES

**Materials.**
1. Microscope
2. Slide and cover slip
3. Toothpick
4. Tincture of iodine
5. Prepared slides of blood, nerve, bone, muscle, and connective tissue

**Test tubes of living cells.** Did you know that animal cells can be grown outside the living body? This capacity was first demonstrated by the Yale biologist Ross Harrison. In the early years of this century he transferred nerve tissue from frog embryos to glass flasks filled with nutrients. The tissue continued to grow for several days. From this simple start, a science was born, the science of *tissue culture.* Today, even adult human cells are cultivated in test tubes, and the duration of growth has been extended from days to years.

Tissues, surrounded by nutrients, are started on a foundation of glass or perforated cellophane, or grown as a suspension within the nutrient liquid itself. The nourishment must be constantly circulated so that fresh food is always available. This is commonly accomplished by putting tissue tubes in a rotating drum. The tubes are stoppered to prevent bacterial contamination, and penicillin is often added for the same purpose.

Supplying the correct nutrients upon which cells will develop and reproduce is no easy task. Usually some natural body fluid such as the serum of blood is added, but artificial culture mixtures containing large numbers of chemicals and vitamins are gaining in popularity as more is learned about exact tissue needs.

Although individual types of cells will propagate, there is no way of combining them to get whole organs or animals, at least not at present. In the meantime, we need not resort to science fiction to find applications. The technique helps biologists discover the responses of cells to radiation, temperature, and drugs. This has been particularly important to researchers working with cancer.

**Dissecting the invisible.** The cells of our body are so small as to be completely invisible to the naked eye. But scientists, peering through microscopes, have been operating on just such cells since 1859. Today, microsurgeons take out the centrally placed nucleus of a living cell with the precision of a macrosurgeon removing a human appendix.

To do this work one must, of course, use special miniature tools. One investigator has said that "an operation on a cell with the point of the finest sewing needle by the steadiest human hand would be like trying to shave a man's face with a bulldozer." Fortunately, sewing needles are not employed, but instead one depends on glass rods heated and drawn to invisible points. In a *micromanipulator* one twists, screws or makes other motions which bring such a glass point to the cell for cutting or puncturing. In another procedure, glass is drawn into a hollow tube, the *micropipette*. Through this tube, scientists suck out cell parts or inject various fluids into its insides.

Microsurgery has helped researchers discover many of the small things of life which make the bigger things possible. In their laboratories they have measured muscle strength by watching the movement of two glass points stuck at opposite ends of a single muscle cell. They have injected dyes which alter color to indicate changes of acidity. They have electrically stimulated individual nerve fibers, taken cell temperatures, and performed other marvelous feats in the realm of the invisible.

**The microscope and how it is used.** Apparently men of the Middle Ages did not maintain very high standards of cleanliness, for the magnifying lens, technically a *simple* (one lens) *microscope,* was at this time used solely as a means of locating body parasites. The magnifiers, of which there were several styles, including jeweled ones for the wealthy, were appropriately named "flea glasses."

Antonj van Leeuwenhoek, a seventeenth-century biologist, brought simple lenses to near perfection. Eventually he achieved magnifications of up to 270 times normal size. He had little faith, however, in the *compound* (two lens) *microscopes* which had been developed by his predecessors, Jansen and Galileo. Van Leeuwenhoek misjudged their value, for this microscope is today's popular model and the one which we shall now examine.

Look at a compound microscope and at Fig. 2–1. The instrument has two lenses, placed such that the upper one magnifies the image of the lower. The one at the top of the *tube* is called an *ocular lens* and that at

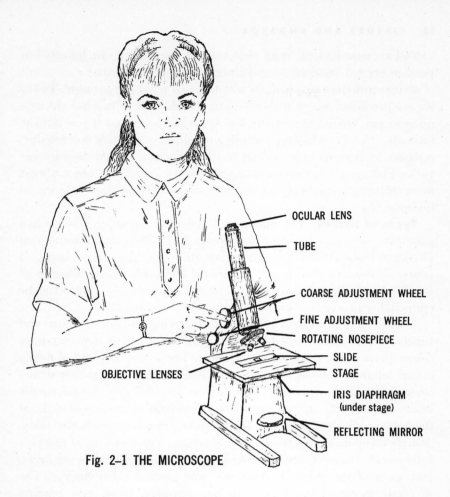

OCULAR LENS

TUBE

COARSE ADJUSTMENT WHEEL

FINE ADJUSTMENT WHEEL

ROTATING NOSEPIECE

SLIDE

OBJECTIVE LENSES

STAGE

IRIS DIAPHRAGM
(under stage)

REFLECTING MIRROR

Fig. 2–1 THE MICROSCOPE

the bottom an *objective lens*. Often there are two or more objectives, each with different powers of enlargement. To change powers, revolve the *nosepiece* until the desired objective is aligned with the tube.

To use the microscope, put a hair or some other small object in the center of a rectangular glass *slide* and clamp it in place on the stage. Rotate the *reflecting mirror,* under the stage, until strong light is directed on the object. Adjust the *diaphragm,* between the mirror and stage, to reduce this light to a desirable level. Now turn the *coarse adjustment wheel* cautiously to bring your lowest power objective to within one quarter inch of the slide. Draw the tube slowly upward till focus is achieved. Switch to a higher power objective, if desired, making sure that the lens and slide do not come in contact. Revolve the *fine adjustment wheel* to explore minute details.

You are now looking at an object which is enlarged one hundred or perhaps several hundred times its normal size. Imagine the excitement of seventeenth-century scientists who first saw what you see now. Today we are privileged to use not only optical tools such as this but electron microscopes, enlarging 100,000 diameters or more, and this is not the ultimate. The French have recently completed a protonic microscope, a device so powerful that it can theoretically resolve the distance between hydrogen and oxygen atoms of a water molecule. These almost inconceivable magnifications are very revealing for those trained in their use.

**Types of tissues.** You may give a violent exclamation when a nail penetrates your bare foot and blood pours forth. Why does it hurt? You hit nerve tissue. What else did it pass through? Skin and muscle, of course. If the nail goes deeply, it may hit bone. These are examples of the five basic animal tissues: (1) blood, (2) nerve, (3) protective or epithelial, (4) muscle, and (5) supportive or connective.

A *tissue* is defined as a group of cells having similar structure and function. The term is used loosely. Often we speak of bony or fatty tissue. In truth these are both connective. The actual divisions of tissues are as follows. *Blood* is solid red cells floating in a transparent straw-colored liquid, the plasma. *Nerve* tissue includes cells found in the brain, spinal cord, and all nerves. *Epithelial* tissue consists of cells on the surface of the body and lining passageways through the body. *Muscle* tissue makes up the bulk of arms and legs, swelling as one performs work. It also includes similar contractile tissue found in the heart, and walls of the stomach, intestines, and certain other organs. The divisions of *connective* tissue are fat, cartilage, bone, and binding materials between bones and around organs.

## EXAMINATION OF CELLS FROM THE CHEEK

Scrape the inner lining of the cheek with the blunt end of a toothpick or similar device. Place the scrapings in a drop of water on a slide and cover with a small thin *cover glass*. Lower this gently into place to exclude air bubbles. The cells from the cheek are flattened epithelial with small spherical structures in the center called *nuclei*. The edges of the cells may be somewhat folded (Fig. 2–2).

Touch a minute drop of iodine to the edge of the cover glass. The color will pass under by capillary attraction and stain the cells, especially the nuclei. *Histologists,* those who prepare and study tissues, stain their slides to enhance detail or to make previously imperceptible parts visible.

A common procedure involves the tinting of thin tissue slices with hematoxylin and eosin dyes, which color some parts of a cell pink and other parts blue.

**Study of prepared slides.** Carefully examine prepared slides of blood, nerve (the spinal-cord smear from an ox is illustrated here), bone, muscle, and connective tissue (Fig. 2–2). Note similarities of nuclei but variations in the size and shapes of cells. The material surrounding the nucleus is called *cytoplasm*. The covering of each cell is a *cell membrane*. Many cells will be grouped together to form the separate tissues.

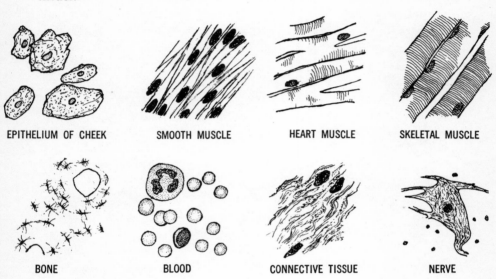

EPITHELIUM OF CHEEK    SMOOTH MUSCLE    HEART MUSCLE    SKELETAL MUSCLE

BONE    BLOOD    CONNECTIVE TISSUE    NERVE

Fig. 2–2 COMMON TISSUES OF THE BODY

## OTHER THINGS TO DO

The closer we approach an object the larger it appears. Unfortunately the human eye has limitations in this respect. Youngsters can focus on objects a few inches from the eye, but as we grow older this distance recedes. However, one can see clearly at a lesser distance if he gets light rays only from the center of an object. Demonstrate this by punching a hole in a piece of cardboard or paper with the tip of a needle. With your eye near the hole, look at print from about a two-inch distance. Are the words enlarged?

You can make good permanent mounts of hair, feathers, scales, insect parts, and other simple objects. Place your specimen in a drop of xylol which has been encircled with balsam on a microscope slide. Cover with a cover slip to complete the mounting.

Very thin slices of liver, heart, muscle, kidney, and other organs may be obtained through use of a device called the *microtome* (both hand and machine types are available) or even a sharp razor. The slices may be magnified and examined as is, but staining helps bring out the details. The somewhat complicated procedure for this is described in J. D. Corrington's *Exploring with Your Microscope,* McGraw-Hill Book Company, Inc., New York, 1957. This book also contains a number of other projects worthy of your consideration.

# Animals Without Backbones

3

## THE SMALLEST ANIMALS

**Materials.**
1. Water containing living amoebas, paramecia, and/or other protozoa
2. Slides and cover slips
3. Microscope
4. Yeast

**The discovery of invisible animals.** In 1674 the world of the smallest animals was seen for the first time. Using hand-ground lenses, Antonj van Leeuwenhoek made observations which eventually opened an entirely new field of science, *protozoology,* the study of single-celled animals. The tiny creatures called *protozoa* are almost all invisible to the unaided eye. With microscopes, however, Leeuwenhoek and later scientists uncovered many details of their previously private lives.

**Protozoa, life-givers and life-takers.** Curiously enough, the very existence of the largest of all creatures depends on small animal life. One-hundred-foot long blue whales have, instead of teeth, rows of whalebone extending down from their upper jaws. The whalebone strains out millions of animal and plant cells which are used for food. Protozoa are an important ingredient of the whale diet.

Another animal, the wood-eating termite, relies on protozoa. An intriguing problem for many years was how this animal could subsist on its particular ration. Wood contains mostly cellulose, an indigestible material. The mystery was solved when microscopic animals were found in the termite's intestine. The protozoa ingest bits of wood and convert this to soluble carbohydrates. Part is used by the protozoa and part by its host. Should extermination be aimed at the protozoa rather than the termite? It's worth thinking about.

Not all tiny animals are friendly. The dread African sleeping sickness is spread by trypanosomes, invisible residents of the tsetse fly. Another disease infecting man is malaria, a very common killer. In India it causes over one million deaths annually. In the United States it is still prevalent in the South. Malaria is caused by a group of protozoa called plasmodia. Plasmodia are inhabitants of the anopheles mosquito. Its bite spreads the disease.

**Small but tough.** If numbers are important, protozoa win over all. There are more protozoa than all other animals and, what's more, they are found in more places. Protozoa are on and under land, in fresh and salt water, inside animals, and floating high in the air. Unpleasant localities are no problem. Beneath the ice of the coldest seas grow certain of these pigmies. Hot springs are the bathing places for others. Even the more common types can survive drying and heat exposure by forming a shell about their exterior which prevents evaporation. In this condition they are known as *cysts*. Cysts attach to birds' feet or are blown by the wind, spreading protozoa from one pond to another.

**Animal nomenclature and classes of protozoa.** There are about one million distinctly different animal types in our world, and an additional third of a million plants. In order to study the multitudes of life in an organized manner, biologists have had to work out a system of classification.* In this system a large distinct group is called a *phylum;* for instance, Protozoa is the phylum containing single-celled animals. The next major division is called a *class*. The smallest distinguishable group is called a *specie*. Thousands of species are contained in the phylum *Protozoa*.

There are four important classes of Protozoa: (1) the amoeboid protozoa, (2) the ciliates, (3) the flagellates, and (4) the spore-formers. The *amoeboid protozoa* are shapeless, irregular cells having jellylike extensions from the main cell body called *pseudopods*. These push out first in one direction, then in another, helping the tiny animals creep along and occasionally engulfing food. The *amoeba* is typical of this class (Fig. 3–1). The *ciliates* are those protozoa having numerous, very small, hairlike projections about their bodies. By waving these *cilia* they glide about much in the manner of a boat rowed by oars. A representative ciliate is the one called *paramecium* (Fig. 3–2). The

* For a more complete discussion, see Appendix C, which also lists several of the major phyla.

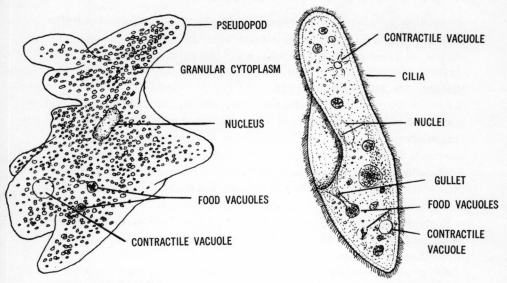

Fig. 3-1 AN AMOEBA

Fig. 3-2 A PARAMECIUM

*flagellates* are miscroscopic animals, each of which bears one or more whiplike appendages called flagella. The protozoa propel themselves by "cracking the whip." An example of this class is *Euglena* (Fig. 3-3). The *spore-formers* are parasitic animals, usually without a means of

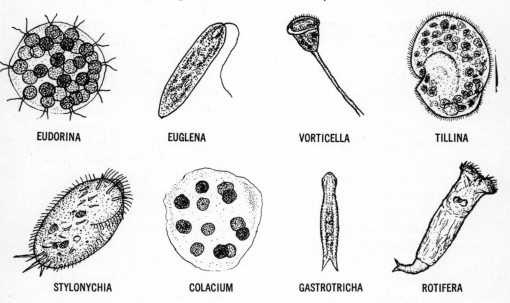

EUDORINA          EUGLENA          VORTICELLA          TILLINA

STYLONYCHIA          COLACIUM          GASTROTRICHA          ROTIFERA

Fig. 3-3 COMMON MICROSCOPIC ANIMALS IN POND WATER

locomotion or any particular structure for obtaining food. Typically they are found in the digestive tract of animals. The malaria and sleeping-sickness parasites are examples of this class.

## WHERE TO FIND PROTOZOA

Obtain samples of water and decaying pond plants from several local ponds and neighborhood ditches. Include a bit of the surface scum. The samples may be examined at once, but greater concentrations of protozoa result if they are allowed to stand in open containers for one or two weeks, during which time they reproduce. This is especially true if a little boiled lettuce is added to the water. Bacteria feed on the lettuce, and protozoa feed on the bacteria.

Particular species such as amoeba and paramecium may or may not be present in your sample. If wanted, order from one of the biological supply houses listed in Appendix E.

**Observing protozoa.** Study carefully diagrams of some of the various common protozoa (Figs. 3–1, 3–2, and 3–3). With a medicine dropper, obtain a drop or two of water from the bottom of the pond-water container. Place this on a slide and cover gently with a cover slip, excluding all air bubbles. Look for and identify under low and high magnification as many of the protozoa as possible. Keep the light from the mirror somewhat reduced for best observation. Obtain another sample of water near the surface. Are other species of protozoa present?

**Anatomy of the amoeba (Fig. 3–1).** The amoeba is an irregularly shaped, transparent cell which slowly and constantly changes shape. Watch this movement for two or three minutes. Sketch the amoeba at different time intervals and record the time with each drawing.

The amoeba, as do most other cells, consists of two basic portions, a nucleus and cytoplasm. The *nucleus* is a slightly darker, centrally located mass, rather difficult to distinguish. The *cytoplasm* is the very abundant, transparent, granular material lying between the nucleus and the outer

Vacuoles are small, spherical containers within the cytoplasm which hold either water or food. Identify the empty-looking, water-holding *contractile vacuoles*. These pump out excess water which enters the cell. *Pseudopods* of streaming cytoplasm engulf small life forms upon which the amoeba feeds. When this occurs, *food vacuoles* form and the food is digested.

Respiration and excretion are elementary processes in amoebas and other protozoa. Oxygen is absorbed directly from water through the cell membrane.

cell membrane. Carbon dioxide and other waste products are excreted from the cell back into the water. Reproduction is brought about simply by dividing into two parts, a process called *fission*.

**Studying the paramecium (Fig. 3–2).** Place a drop of water containing paramecia on a slide. Observe the dashing, whirling, swimming motion of these slipper-shaped protozoans. Watch the animals back up as they meet obstructions. See how they continue their efforts till they find a clear path.

Add to the protozoa a drop of yeast dissolved in water. Watch how yeast cells are drawn by barely visible cilia down the *gullet* to form a food vacuole. After a few moments, the first vacuole breaks off and another forms.

Locate within the paramecium the following structures: (1) nuclei, (2) cytoplasm, (3) cell membrane, and (4) contractile vacuoles. Two faint nuclei are present in most species of paramecia as opposed to one in the amoeba. More than one contractile vacuole may also be present. Allow the slide and paramecia to dry partially. This alters their shape but makes easier the examination of contractile vacuoles. Watch as these transparent globes fill and empty. Radiating canals are sometimes seen at the sides like points of stars.

## OTHER THINGS TO DO

Just a glance at pond-water protozoa introduces entire new concepts, but details are available only to those who spend time in their pursuit. Get a good book like T. L. Jahn and F. F. Jahn, *How to Know the Protozoa,* W. C. Brown, Dubuque, 1950. Learn to recognize as many species as possible. There are thousands of these, including special kinds in frog or termite intestines and newt blood. Do not confuse rotifers or gastrotrichs (Fig. 3–3) with protozoa. They belong to a distinct, more complex phylum.   .

Perhaps photography is one of your hobbies. If so, you will probably want to snap a few pictures through the microscope. Use stationary objects such as prepared slides of protozoa, fish scales, insect "feelers," and so forth. Turn strong light on the specimen and get it in focus. Hold a piece of paper above the microscope tube to find the point at which light from the mirror makes the smallest, most distinct spot. Clamp the camera in place with its lens at this point. Make a lightproof connection between it and the microscope. Focus for a distance shot. Open the diaphragm. Expose for several seconds; the exact time varies, of course, with your particular lighting conditions.

# 4
# HYDRA—THE HARMLESS SERPENT

**Materials.**
1. Living hydra
2. Hand lens and/or microscope
3. Watch glass or small beaker
4. Snail or slug meat

**The first multicellular animals.** The beginnings of life involved only very small single-celled organisms, each independent of every other. Judging by numbers, this was and is one of Nature's most successful experiments. Countless cells of this type are still present in almost every part of our world, in water and soil and as parasites in other animals.

As organisms evolved, their cells grouped together for greater efficiency. Individual cells acquired specific functions rather than carrying on all functions. Such simple features are well illustrated in modern-day Volvox. This creature is a colonial organization of thousands of individual microscopic cells. Together they form a small, floating green ball about the size of a pinhead. Each cell is connected to every other cell by extensions of body material. The entire co-ordinated mass is capable of swimming about and capturing food. Similar but less complex organizations are found in Eudorina and Colacium (Fig. 3–3). More advanced, but still very primitive, are sponges (yes, these are animals) and coelenterates, the jellyfish and its relatives. The relatives include hydra, and with this our story begins.

**Hydra, Hercules, and "frayed strings."** Take a small piece of string, unravel one end, and you have a pretty good representation of hydra (Fig. 4–1). The animal, when extended, has the diameter of a thread and shows five or six hairlike tentacles projected outward like the arms of an octopus. It stretches out to about half an inch in length.

The name hydra is derived from the monstrous nine-headed serpent of Greek mythology which goes by the same name. Eight of the heads were mortal, but the ninth grew back as two heads each time it was cut off. Hercules finally slayed the monster by burning and burying the heads.

Modern hydras are hardly to be feared, yet in regenerative power they are even more remarkable than their namesake. When cut in many pieces, they become just as many hydras. In this respect they are much like their indestructible but more highly evolved associates, the flatworms (Chapter 5).

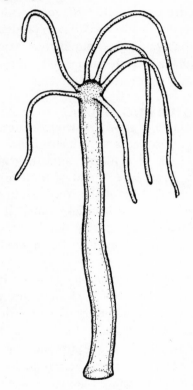

Fig. 4–1 HYDRA

**The private life of hydra.** When a small animal swims nearby, hydra grasps and hugs it in a tentacle embrace. Special cells called *nematocysts* discharge poisonous barbs into the intruder. The food is then drawn to the mouth, which relaxes and allows entry into the hollow inside. In this cavity it is digested and fed to cells lining the cavity. Conveniently, the body wall of hydra is only two cell layers thick. Therefore, every cell is within easy reach of the food.

When disturbed, a hydra rapidly contracts into a small speck of lightly tinted jelly. The slightest touch is detected and transmitted through a network of nerves. Muscle cells in the walls bring about this contraction. Even the tentacles are drawn in.

Reproduction sometimes involves sex differences and sometimes does not. Commonly the species is propagated asexually by *budding*. One or two small hydra bud out from the old body just as limbs bud from a tree. These break off within a few days to form new animals. In sexual reproduction, *sperm* from the male *testis* joins with the *egg* from the female *ovary* to generate a new animal. The reproductive organs will be recognized as small bumps on the body if they happen to be present. Sometimes hydra will have both sperm and eggs, a condition called *hermaphroditism*.

## PROCEDURE FOR STUDYING HYDRA

Look for hydra in lakes or slowly moving streams. They will usually be found attached to water weeds a few inches below the surface. Hydra are not easily recognized. Movements cause their abrupt withdrawal. In this condition they can be felt and seen as faint gray or brown jellylike masses. Break off some of the weed. Hold it quietly near the water surface or place it in a bottle of lake water. If hydra are present, they will soon extend outward, perpendicular to the weed surface. When these are not readily found, they may be ordered from one of the biological supply houses.

Place a live specimen in a watch glass or small beaker and observe with a magnifying lens. Watch for spontaneous movements of the tentacles. Now place a very minute piece of snail or slug meat (or a small water animal, Daphnia, its favorite food) near the tentacles. The tentacles will slowly reach out and grasp the object. Food is drawn into the mouth at the free end. From here it passes into the expanded gut for digestion. If not completely digested, a portion will be excreted back through the mouth.

## OTHER THINGS TO DO

The discharge of slender, needlelike nematocysts may be observed by placing a hydra in water on a slide under a microscope. Allow the animal to extend. Stick a toothpick into acetic acid or vinegar and touch this to the edge of the water. As acid diffuses about its tentacles, hydra explodes numerous stinging barbs.

If your hydra do not have ovaries and testes, you may want to purchase prepared slides of the organs or repeat some of the experiments described by W. F. Loomis in "The sex gas of hydra," *Scientific American*, 200:145, April 1959. Loomis observed that when overcrowded hydra are left in stale aquarium water, they start reproducing sexually, the result of an increased pressure of dissolved carbon dioxide gas.

For more information about invertebrates we recommend R. Buchsbaum, *Animals Without Backbones,* University of Chicago Press, Chicago, 1948; for more experiments see E. C. Cole, "Antidote for formalin," *The American Biology Teacher,* 16:201, December 1954, and 17:78, February 1955. These sources suggest numerous projects which you may perform with protozoa, hydra, worms, clams, crayfish, and other creatures.

# 5
## INDESTRUCTIBLE FLATWORMS

**Materials.**
1. Living planaria and pond water
2. Hand lens and/or microscope
3. Piece of fresh liver or heart
4. Razor blade and beaker or petri dish

**Missing parts replaced by new ones.** An animal is cut in two pieces—each grows into a distinct organism. What kind of monster is this? A flatworm, *planaria,* can regenerate a whole animal from each piece when cut up. If a head is cut off, the body will grow a new head, and the head will form a new body and tail.

This unusual process of regenerating whole bodies is an ability possessed only by less specialized forms of life. The lowly sponge, when passed through a sieve, sometimes rejoins into a whole sponge and at other times becomes many tiny sponges. More complex animals, for instance the crayfish, do not live when cut in two, but may develop limbs in place of lost ones. Man cannot replace missing fingers, but he can grow scar tissue to cover wounds, heal broken bones, and even rejoin cut nerves in favorable locations.

**The necessity of nerve for regeneration.** Biologists have asked why some animals regenerate while others do not. Two favorite animals for investigating this problem have been the salamander and the frog. Both are amphibians, but only the salamander regenerates missing limbs as an adult. It has been found, however, that amputated arms and legs of salamanders will not regrow after the nerve fibers have been destroyed, and that injected chemicals which paralyze nerves have the same effect.

Although adult frogs will not develop lost limbs, tadpoles will regrow amputated tails or arms and legs which have just recently sprouted. Investigators found that the nerve supply of the tadpole is relatively greater than that in adults. With this in mind, they performed a surprising experiment. They cut open an adult frog and maneuvered the large nerve of its hind leg to the surface of the amputated front leg, thus supplementing the nerve supply. What happened? You guessed it. This frog and others like him now regenerated their front limbs, not perfect in size or shape, but at least they were arms. Apparently the nerve secretes some chemical or chemicals which promote regrowth. When this is isolated, there may even be applications to the regeneration of certain human organs or tissues. The idea sounds a little farfetched, but it is worth investigating.

**The necessity of oxygen to orient regeneration.** We return now to the flatworm, planaria, to pick up another clue to regeneration. Biologists who have chopped up the little creatures from head to tail find the head ends grow tails faster and better than the tail ends grow heads. In fact, some planaria absolutely refuse to regenerate heads on pieces sliced from their tails. As a result, we get animals with only one eye or perhaps no eyes at all. What causes this predicament?

Researchers measured the oxygen utilization of each piece and discovered that head pieces consume more of the vital respiratory gas than do tail pieces. This influence on regeneration was further demonstrated by cutting out thin slices from just behind the eyes or way down on the tail. The upper slice grew two heads with no tail, and the lower slice grew two tails with no head. They concluded that since the consumption of oxygen is negligibly different on each side of a thin slice, the animal cannot distinguish the difference and fails to get organized.

The directive role of oxygen has proved significant for embryos in animals of higher species. If chemicals which alter oxygen consumption are added at certain critical stages of development, they cause many abnormalities of form, and these abnormalities are most severe in the suppressed head region.

**Planaria.** The half-inch-long planaria are a drab color, usually dark gray or brown, and may have darker or lighter spots (Fig. 5–1).

PHARYNX

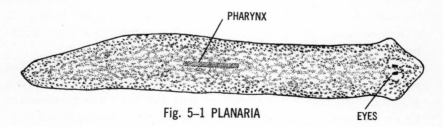

Fig. 5–1 PLANARIA                    EYES

Two light spots on the triangular head are eyes, which appear crossed. Planaria obtain meat and animal matter through a *pharynx* which protrudes out from the middle of the body. They move by *cilia* on their ventral surface in a gliding motion over a mucous trail which they secrete or by muscular wormlike contractions.

Planaria reproduce either sexually or asexually (without sex). Asexual reproduction is brought about by dividing, the posterior or tail part of the worm separating from the anterior or head end. The front part regenerates a new tail and the hind part grows a new head. The worms are hermaphroditic, each having reproductive organs of both sexes.

## COLLECTING AND FEEDING PLANARIA

Look on the bottoms of rocks from streams or lakes for small, soft, jellylike blobs. These are the planaria. At first they are quiet, but soon a few will slip along, seeking darkness. Put planaria in a jar of pond or stream water (tap water may be used if it has stood in an open container for several days) and keep the jar in the dark. Feed them with raw meat once or twice weekly, upon which they will gladly gorge themselves. When they finish eating (one to two hours later), remove the meat and replace the stale water with fresh water.

If you watch your planaria as they feed, you may notice that their interiors become gradually more distinct and colored. This is due to food accumulating in their digestive tracts. The *digestive tract* is in the shape of a Y with one branch running forward and two backward. Numerous smaller tubes project off each side of the three main branches. Food enters through the pharynx at the junction in the middle of the Y. Give the animals a truly bloody meal sometime, fresh liver or heart, and watch the result. Examine with a hand lens or low-power microscope, if available. An intense red hue permeates the tract of all who eat. There will be no mistaking it. How many days does it take to disappear?

If you are not too good about taking care of your planaria, they will get along on their own. After using every speck of nourishment within the digestive tract, they start digesting the lining itself and then go to other cells of the body. They continue this for months, sometimes shrinking to only one sixth of their former size.

**Regeneration experiments.** Put a planaria on a smooth glass plate and cut it in two or more pieces crosswise or lengthwise with a razor blade. Put each piece in a beaker or petri dish filled with pond water. Cover and label the source of each piece. Keep the dish in a dark place and examine every two or three days, adding more water whenever the level goes down. The pieces will start to regenerate, and in about two weeks or less each will have formed a smaller complete planarian. Two-headed planaria may be made by slicing the head in two down to the pharynx and not allowing the two halves to come back together until regeneration is complete. Two- or many-tailed planaria may also be formed by cutting the tail down the center.

## OTHER THINGS TO DO

Darken one side of your planaria container and place a bright light at the other side. This will confirm your observation made while collecting; planaria retreat in the presence of light. Use a dissecting needle to turn one of the animals on its back. It flips over at once, demonstrating a balancing response found throughout the animal kingdom. On its own initiative, however, a planarian will sometimes glide upside down across the upper surface of water.

Try regeneration experiments on sponges, hydra, crayfish, fish, tadpoles, salamanders, and insects. Sometimes only the young of a species will show the regenerative response. For instance, a young praying mantis regrows lost legs, increasing their size with each successive molt, but an old mantis will not do this. Immature walking sticks and some grasshoppers will purposely shed injured legs, then replace them at a later date.

# 6

## FROG FLUKES AND OTHER PARASITES

**Materials.**
1. Frogs
2. Dissecting instruments
3. Microscope or hand lens, slide, and cover slip
4. Sodium chloride (table salt) and finger bowl

**Roundworms, tapeworms, and flukes.** It has been said that if our earth were to vanish totally except for its myriads of roundworms, one could still recognize the shapes of the mountains, hills, lakes, and oceans which they inhabit. There, too, would be the shadowy outlines of the world's plants and animals, for many worms are *parasitic;* they get free food by living within and digesting the tissues of living hosts. The damage which they thus cause is tremendous. The annual loss to American agriculture has been estimated at half a billion dollars.

Even we humans sometimes unwillingly provide homes for roundworms. The intestinal parasite, ascaris, is one of the troublemakers. It is especially frequent in the southeastern United States. Eggs from the adult worm pass out with feces from an infested individual. If sanitary disposal is lacking, animals and people walk upon and spread the eggs. Should these get on unwashed vegetables or unwashed hands they are swallowed with one's food. Inside the intestine they quickly grow to adult worms several inches in length.

Millions of people in the rural United States suffer from hookworms, another of man's numerous parasites. These, too, are spread by unsanitary fecal disposal. The worms have an efficient means of entering the human body; they burrow through bare feet. The simple expedient of wearing shoes solves the problem of their entry.

Inhabitants of the Orient have enriched their soil for centuries with human wastes. The advantages to crop production are apparent, and the advantages for spreading parasites are even more apparent. The blood fluke, a flatworm relative of planaria (Chapter 5), is particularly well distributed among the Chinese and Japanese. In planting rice, they stand barelegged in watery fields. Young of the flukes enter through the skin and are carried by the blood stream to the intestinal wall where they grow and mate.

Parasitic worms are sometimes carried in edible meats. The meats must be thoroughly cooked to destroy them. Trichina, the microscopic inhabitant of pork, is one of these. If inadequately cooked pork is eaten, the worms enter the intestine and bear young. The young leave the intestine via the blood stream and bore into human muscle where they cause intense pain and fever. Poorly cooked pork and beef may also contain tapeworms; the Chinese get liver flukes similarly by eating raw fish.

Filaria is a tropical worm transported by mosquitoes. When an infected mosquito bites, it allows filaria to enter and block lymph glands and vessels. The blockage sometimes causes a human leg to swell to the size of an elephant's. The condition is appropriately named elephantiasis.

A serious African pest is the guinea worm. This long, narrow creature lives near the surface of the skin, forming a blister which erupts to release the young. These contaminate the river water where women wash their clothing. Native medicine men have learned to remove the adults successfully by winding them out on a stick. Unfortunately, a serious infection often results unless the wound is treated with modern medicines.

## Who's who among the parasites

Big fleas have little fleas
Upon their backs to bite 'em,
And little fleas have lesser fleas,
And so, *ad infinitum*.

Not only are fleas and roundworms *parasites* but throughout the animal and plant kingdoms there are little bread beggars who far outnumber their hosts. Many of these dependents produce toxins, block lymph vessels, feed on tissues, or otherwise make themselves obnoxious. In its most inclusive sense, the term parasite embraces even the viruses, so unbelievably small that they are seen only in photographs by electron microscopes. Viruses cause smallpox, yellow fever, flu, polio, measles, mumps, and the common cold. Somewhat larger are bacteria which transmit plague, dysentery, diphtheria, leprosy, cholera, and other objectionable diseases. Larger but still invisible are protozoa which bring malaria and sleeping sickness. And finally there are worms, ticks, and chiggers. Ours is assuredly a world of "uninvited guests."

There are organisms, closely related to parasites, which are not "bad" at all. One such group, the *symbionts,* form an indispensable partnership with their host. The termite, as previously mentioned, has protozoa in its intestines which digest wood. Without them, he sickens and dies despite a full belly. Another group, the *commensals,* are non-essential but convenient. The hermit crab and sea anemone are such examples. The crab chooses for his home an unoccupied snail shell. Along comes a sea anemone which settles on the shell. This makes a dandy arrangement. The anemone provides camouflage, and the crab procures most of the food.

**The Black Death, or Plague.** Bacterial warfare is a concept not entirely new to modern times. In the fourteenth century a battle raged between the Genoese and Tartars. The Tartars were overcome by a violent sickness, causing fevers, chills, excruciating pains, vomiting, and usually death. Their undoing became disaster for the Genoese as well, for they hurled plague-killed corpses into the camp of the enemy. The Genoese sailed to escape this affliction, but wherever they docked, plague docked with them. Eventually about a third of the European population was destroyed in this epidemic which history calls the Black Death.

Plague is a disease of rats and fleas. On occasion, enormous numbers of rats succumb to an overwhelming invasion of the bacteria. Fleas leaving dead and dying rats turn to and infect humans. Epidemics of this nature have occurred often since the Dark Ages, only recently coming under control through sanitation, anti-rat campaigns, and streptomycin. Infrequent cases in the western United States are now attributed to fleas of squirrels as well as those of rats.

**Yellow Fever and Major Reed.** In 1899, American troops in Cuba suffered from a most discomforting disease. The chief symptoms were nausea, fever, and yellow skin. A commission was formed, with Major Walter Reed in charge, to investigate the cause of the fever. Believing that mosquitoes might be at fault, commission members allowed themselves to be bitten by those insects which previously had fed on yellow-fever victims. The volunteers soon developed the disease and one died. Others slept on sheets and in pajamas soiled by yellow-fever patients. None became sick so long as they were screened from mosquitoes.

Reed's experiments proved without doubt that the Aëdes mosquito was the culprit, and steps were taken for its elimination. Breeding sites were removed or covered. Patients and troops were surrounded by wire screening. As a result, yellow fever almost completely disappeared in a few months' time.

**The battle continues.** Polio has been a dreaded pestilence of modern times, especially in the United States. Research workers were handicapped by the inability of the virus to grow on or in anything but humans. Finally, in 1949, successful cultures were established on monkey kidneys. Dr. Jonas Salk devised a method for killing kidney-grown virus with formaldehyde, while not disturbing its ability to produce with polio-resisting antibodies within the injected subject's body. The vaccine, proven safe and eighty per cent effective, was quickly brought into mass production. This and the more recent oral vaccines now protect many of us from crippling paralysis.

The importance of medical research and preparedness was illustrated again in 1957 during an Asian flu epidemic. Over 20,000,000 individuals were victimized in the United States, being overcome by fever, nausea, aches, and great weakness. Earlier investigations had shown that the virus could be cultivated in large quantities on embryonic eggs. This was accomplished swiftly, mass inoculations were given which prevented further infection.

Since 1900 the average life expectancy of newborn infants in this country has increased from forty-nine to seventy years of age. Certainly, modern medical research, vaccination efforts, and an enormous improvement in sanitary standards have all been important in making this possible. In the future many other critical diseases will probably be added to the list of those already successfully conquered.

## HOW TO FIND FROG FLUKES

A convenient animal for parasite studies is the frog. Procure one or more (preferably more) from nature's store or a biological dealer. In order not to waste animal life, we suggest using only frogs which have been submitted to other experimental studies, for instance those on nerve and digestion in this book. Avoid frogs which have been captives for more than one or two weeks. They sometimes shed their parasites in these circumstances, especially if unfed.

Double pith the animal as described in Chapter 16. Open the chest wall. On each side of the body cavity will appear an inflated, hollow, elongated lung, well supplied with blood vessels. Cut the lungs free at the head end and place them in a finger bowl or cup of saline solution.*

---

* For frogs, flukes, and other "cold-blooded" animals, saline is made by dissolving 0.7 gm. of sodium chloride (table salt) in 100 ml. of water. For warm-blooded animals you use 0.9 gm. salt/100 ml. The difference results from a variation in the salt concentration of their tissues.

Pull the tissue apart to see the wiggling worms inside. With luck, you will find both flat-bodied worms, the *flukes* or *trematodes,* and round-bodied *roundworms* or *nematodes*. Two common and fairly typical types are Haematoloechus and Rhabdias (Figs. 6–1 and 6–2). Either of these may be up to half an inch in length.

Flukes have suckers for attaching to host tissues. In loosening them from lungs, entire head ends are apt to be lost unless one concentrates first on freeing these suckers. Try shaking the lungs to make them let go.

Place your specimens on a slide and cover with a cover slip. Examine with low power of a microscope or with a hand lens. Notice the digestive tube: *mouth, pharynx,* and *intestine*. The latter divides and ends blindly in Haematoloechus. Do you see contractions and movements of food in the intestine?

Observe the immensely developed reproductive system: *ovaries, testes,* and *uterus*. Both sexes are present in a single Haematoloechus but only one in Rhabdias (the male's reproductive opening is near the anus; the female's, at the center of her body). *Yolk glands* nourish *eggs,* often so numerous that they distend the uterus and obscure other struc-tures. This is frustrating for the student, but fortunate for the worm, who is striving only to continue the species. Watch for eggs being ex-pelled through the uterine opening. Occasionally these hatch right on the slide!

## OTHER THINGS TO DO

Not all frog lungs are infested with parasites. If your specimen has none, examine other organs. Include the urinary bladder (Fig. 29–1) and abdominal cavity. A protozoan parasite, Opalina, inhabits the in-testine. Look also in other animals with which you experiment.

Some roundworms are free-living, being most plentiful in moist soil and leaf litter. They may be gathered from soil supported by screen wire and cheesecloth near the top of a funnel. Connect a test tube to the funnel stem with rubber tubing. Pour warmed water (about 40°C.) into the funnel until it fills to the bottom of the soil. Tiny nematodes will now leave their earth and descend into the test tube from which they may be removed for study after a few hours. Other methods for gathering small life are described by L. C. Stegeman, "Some simple techniques for collecting various invertebrate animals for class use," *Turtox News,* 36:8, January 1958. This monthly bulletin of the General Biological Supply House has frequent suggestions for worth-while biological projects.

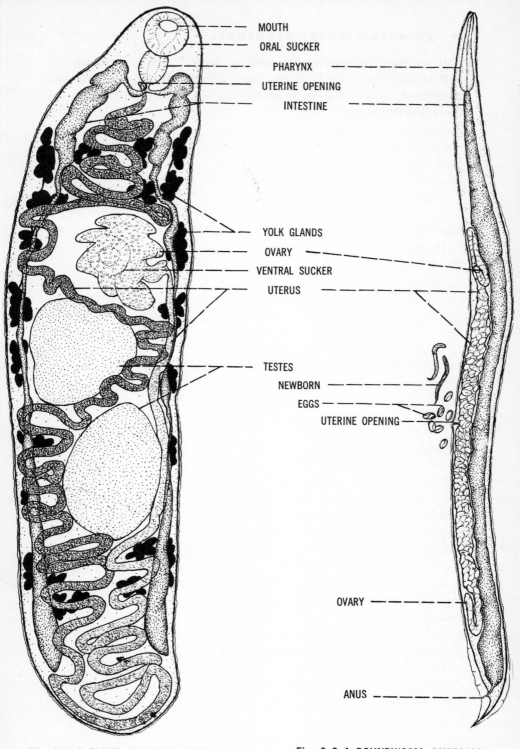

MOUTH
ORAL SUCKER
PHARYNX
UTERINE OPENING
INTESTINE

YOLK GLANDS
OVARY
VENTRAL SUCKER
UTERUS

TESTES
NEWBORN
EGGS
UTERINE OPENING

OVARY

ANUS

Fig. 6–1 A FLUKE, HAEMATOLOECHUS

Fig. 6–2 A ROUNDWORM, RHABDIAS

If you have the opportunity, read the delightful book about the soil and its inhabitants by P. Farb, *Living Earth,* Harper and Brothers, New York, 1959. Free-living nematodes are among the animals described in its chapters.

# Insects and Heredity

---

## 7
## COLLECTING INSECTS

**Materials.**
1. Insect net (made of broomstick, coat hanger, and mosquito netting)
2. Collection box
3. Insect pins
4. Carbon tetrachloride and medicine dropper
5. Mounting board

**Numbers and age of insects.** "Katy-did; Katy-didn't." This call and the shrill chirp of crickets abound on summer evenings. These are the sounds of two of the many common insects. Butterflies flitting from flower to flower, ants on the sidewalk and in yards, and ladybird beetles in the garden are often seen. It would be hard to find an area with no insects—they are everywhere: in the air, on the ground, and in the water. There are more insects on earth than all other non-microscopic animals combined. Compared with the 200,000 kinds of other animals, there are 600,000 different insects! And each year many more are described and named.

Fossil insects have been found preserved in a resin called amber from ancient pine trees, or buried and changed to stone. Two hundred million years ago giant dragonflies with two-foot wing spreads flew over ponds and streams. Ants similar to the ones we see today were building nests 40,000,000 years ago. Man is very young by comparison—he has been on earth for only one million years.

**Characteristics of insects and their relatives.** An insect is an *arthropod,* which means "jointed leg." This phylum also includes spiders, crayfish, crabs, centipedes, and millipedes. Insects differ from their relatives in number of legs. They have six, as opposed to eight in spiders, ten in crayfish and crabs, and so many in centipedes and millipedes that we usually do not bother to count. Arthropods have *exoskeletons,* hard outer coats of armor which imprison and safeguard their inhabitants. As the animal increases in size, the armor must be shed, or molted.

Insect bodies have three divisions: *head, thorax,* and *abdomen.* The three pairs of legs and the wings attach to their thorax. There are usually four wings, but some have only two and others none at all. Most insects have a pair of *compound,* honeycomblike *eyes, antennae* or "feelers," and tiny holes in the sides called *spiracles,* through which they breathe.

**Insect orders and oddities (Fig. 7–1).** The cicadas, insects whose low hum announces summer evenings, are a favorite prey of birds and a particular wasp called the cicada killer. Perhaps you have seen this large wasp sting a cicada and then scoot up a tree for take-off. The weight is great but soon our killer reaches her burrow. The cicada, still alive but paralyzed, is the recipient of an egg which later hatches and eats its host. Vital organs are the last to be devoured. This keeps the cicada living and fresh till the bitter end.

Cicada killers are members of the *Hymenoptera,* one of over thirty orders of the class *Insecta.* Besides wasps, this order includes bees and ants. Many of these are "social" animals, joining in hives and nests. Hymenoptera are the only insects with "stingers," a point which most of us beware.

Cicadas themselves belong to an order of sloping-winged insects called *Homoptera.* This group also contains the leafhoppers and the honeydew secreting aphids so well loved by ants (Chapter 9).

For beauty and elegance, moths and butterflies are rarely, if ever, surpassed. Butterflies are abroad during the day, while moths fly mostly by night. Antennae of the former are slender and knobbed, those of the latter feathery or hairlike. Caterpillars of both suborders and cocoons of moths are easily identified features of this order, *Lepidoptera.*

A common pet in biology classrooms is the praying mantis, a member of the *Orthoptera.* This order also includes other insects with chewing mouthparts: grasshoppers, roaches, katydids, crickets, and walking sticks. Egg cases of the praying mantis may be found or purchased. In the spring, one small mantis after another will emerge. The little fellows are quick to catch fruit flies or other insects. They molt several times to reach an adult size of up to four inches.

The largest group of insects are the hard-winged *Coleoptera,* an

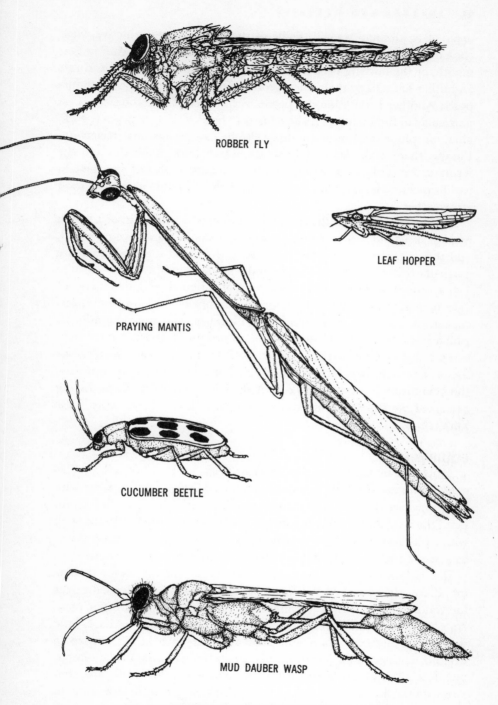

ROBBER FLY

LEAF HOPPER

PRAYING MANTIS

CUCUMBER BEETLE

MUD DAUBER WASP

Fig. 7-1 REPRESENTATIVES OF FIVE INSECT ORDERS

order of beetles and weevils. Some of these have very distinctive, well-chosen names, such as the common May beetle, always out during that month, or the burying beetle. These insects can and do move dead rats and other animals to their underground homes for egg-depositing purposes. Another is the cigarette beetle, a gourmet of fine tobaccos. Less particular in food matters is the drugstore beetle. He eats pepper, cork, glue, morphine, and most anything else he can get his little feelers on. Finally, there is the lead cable beetle, which bores holes through the insulation of cables and lays eggs within, mistakenly identifying these as tree branches. Her popularity decreases as short circuits increase during wet weather.

*Diptera* is an order of flies and mosquitoes, two-winged insects which most of us would just as soon do without. As pests they have no equal, and they often transmit deadly germs. Their blood-sucking habits are particularly distressful for livestock and wildlife.

Six orders of insects have now been mentioned and there are, of course, many more worth learning. Limitations of space prevent a discussion of true bugs, dragonflies, mayflies, lice, and termites, animals which must be separated into five more orders. If you are interested, consult the beginner's guide by H. S. Zim and C. Cottam, *Insects,* Simon and Schuster, New York, 1956. For more advanced work, use the beautifully illustrated book by A. B. Klots and E. B. Klots, *Living Insects of the World,* Doubleday & Company, Inc., Garden City, New York, 1959.

## EQUIPMENT

A net will be needed to catch flying insects such as butterflies. This may be purchased or can be made from an old broom handle, some wire such as a coat hanger, and some mosquito netting or very fine cloth. Bend the wire into a circle ten inches or larger and attach it to the stick with nails or more wire. Sew the netting to the wire with an extra thickness at the top for wear. Make the net about one yard in length.

Use carbon tetrachloride or chloroform to kill the insects for mounting. Place a few drops on the body of the insect with a medicine dropper for simple killing within a minute or so. A killing jar is often used. An old wide-mouthed peanut-butter jar works very well. Mix a little water with plaster of Paris and pour about an inch in the bottom to dry. For killing, add a few drops of carbon tetrachloride to the plaster, put in a piece of cardboard, drop the insects on the cardboard, and screw on the lid. They pass out quickly but take a considerable time to die. Avoid breathing the vapors of carbon tetrachloride and chloroform.

A mounting board is used to spread the wings of large insects. Make this from an old cigar box or from soft wood. Construct as illustrated in Fig. 7–2. Use a longer board if you want to mount several insects at one time. The slight, troughlike angle of the mounting portion gives a natural flying attitude to the wings of your insects. Pins are stuck through their bodies and into corrugated cardboard or balsa wood placed in the bottom of the mounting board.

**Catching insects.** Insects can be found everywhere: in the air, on the ground, and in the water. A surprisingly large number will be caught during the first collecting period. The best time to collect is in late summer or early fall, but some may be found at all times.

Take the net, killing jar, and a box to put insects in and go for a hike in a field, woods, or your own back yard, or go on a field trip with your friends. Catch butterflies, bees, flies, and flying grasshoppers by sweeping them into the net. Flip the net quickly over the wire loop to imprison the insect. Pinch the thorax (the middle body division) of butterflies and moths. This paralyzes them so they will not flap and damage their fragile wings when they are removed from the net.

Drop several drops of carbon tet on the body of the insect or transfer it to the killing jar. Do not place delicate specimens such as butterflies in the same bottle with beetles or other large, hard-bodied insects. Kill them in separate bottles or at different times. Beetles will kick scales off the wings of butterflies. Soft-bodied insects such as larvae may be dropped directly into seventy to eighty per cent ethyl alcohol and preserved in small vials or dried and preserved as described by F. J. Rohlf, "A new technique in the preserving of soft-bodied insects and spiders," *Turtox News,* 35: 226, October 1957.

**Mounting.** Insects should be mounted the same day they are caught, so that they will not dry in an odd position. Do not use regular straight pins for this purpose. They are too thick and have a tendency to rust. Purchase special, long, narrow insect pins from a supply house. Stick one of these through each insect, leaving enough pin above the specimen to hold onto. Place pins in the middle of the thorax or slightly to the right in most specimens. Pin beetles close to the base of the right wing.

Mount butterflies, moths, and other winged specimens, using insect pins to hold the wings in place. See Fig. 7–2 for the correct method and position. To insure complete drying in this position, leave large specimens on the board for at least a week, and smaller specimens for a few days. With other insects, mount the legs in a natural position. This may

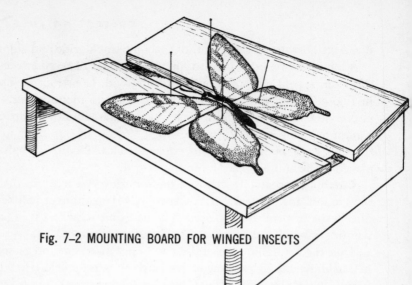

Fig. 7–2 MOUNTING BOARD FOR WINGED INSECTS

be accomplished by sticking the pin with the insect into a small cardboard box until the feet touch the cardboard. Pin the legs in position and allow to dry.

When the insects are dry, put them in a cigar box or glass-topped display case. Place some paradichlorobenzene crystals or moth balls in the box to keep out pests which might destroy the collection. These pests are fellow insects looking for dinner.

Look up each insect and classify it as to order, common name, and/or scientific name. In the display box, arrange the insects under order labels (conveniently made from unlined white index cards). They may be further divided into families if desired.

## OTHER THINGS TO DO

If you like to work with insects, you will profit immensely by the purchase of an inexpensive book by H. Kalmus, 101 *Simple Experiments With Insects,* Doubleday & Company, Inc., Garden City, New York, 1960. Among many other things the author suggests investigation of:

1. Refrigerated insects. Chilling completely halts their movements but heat revives them.
2. Flies in cigarette smoke. Smoke anesthetizes and may even kill them. (A similar reaction occurs in frogs.)
3. Frequency of wingbeats. These are estimated by comparing the wing sounds of insects with the hum of tuning forks or piano cords which vibrate at a known frequency. When pitches of the insect and musical instrument are equal, so are the frequencies.

# 8
# EMERGENCE OF MOTHS

**Materials.**
1. Moth cocoons (or other phases of the life cycle)
2. Scissors

**How the female gets her mate.** From great distances, sometimes up to seven miles, a female moth attracts her opposite member. Biologists suspected for years that this attraction derived from scent glands. Lady moths in the open can easily collect gentlemen, but placed under an odorproof bell jar they lose their lure. The actual verification and isolation of this potent moth perfume evaded chemist's attacks until the late 1950s. At this time, Adolph Butanandt, a former Nobel Prize winner, imported one million silkworm cocoons from Japan and Italy to his laboratories in Germany. He and his associates dissected scent glands from the females, then placed males near various fractions of the glands. When brought to the correct portions, the males fluttered their wings in anticipation. With this knowledge, the scientists eventually isolated the chemical and found its relatively simple formula, $C_{16}H_{30}O$. For all their efforts and all their cocoons, a speck of smell weighing only 1.6 milligrams was obtained, but this was significant. Knowing the structure, they or others will someday develop new, alluring insecticides. These will persuade certain harmful moths into traps and prevent an overabundance of their caterpillars, which destroy tree foliage.

**The emergence and characteristics of adult moths.** The freshly emerged moth has wings which are crumpled and limp. While hanging from his cocoon, the new animal sucks in air and contracts muscles which force fluids into the wings. In about thirty minutes they reach maximal size and then dry as stiffened membranes suitable for flight. At this time the males flutter their wings a bit, then take off in search of the less active females.

Male moths often have large, feathery feelers, or *antennae*. These contain the organs of smell with which they locate females whose antennae are not so feathery. (The antennae also help biologists to separate moths from butterflies. Butterflies have longer, thinner antennae with small knobs at the ends.)

Both sexes of the moth have furry bodies, but the female is quite plump compared with the male. This results from her heavy load of eggs, not from her hearty appetite. As a matter of fact, some adult moths are completely unable to feed and must depend on food stored in their bodies as larvae. This suffices to keep them alive long enough to mate and lay their eggs. Others, such as the hawk moths, have long sucking tubes through which they sip flower nectar. The tube of each moth is coiled beneath his head when not in use.

**Life cycle (Fig. 8–1).** After the female is fertilized, she distributes her *eggs* on some suitable food source. Usually she fastens them to a plant with an adhesive. In occasional species, eggs are scattered without attachment, sometimes during flight.

The *larvae,* or caterpillars, which eat their way out of the eggs, are quite small. But their appetites are large, and through successive molts they attain the sizes with which most of us are familiar. Molts occur each time the animals outgrow their skins. A fluid is secreted which dissolves and separates the outer layer. Eventually it splits free as the body continually expands.

The full-grown larvae of most moth species spin cocoons. Their intricate weaving patterns are co-ordinated by the cerebral hemispheres of very small brains. Experiments with silkworms show that when one hemisphere is removed, silk is spread wherever the worm crawls. If the entire brain is missing, the larva still crawls about but makes no attempt to spin a cocoon.

Inside their cocoons, caterpillars enter a deathlike resting stage and are then known as *pupae.* In this state there is no eating, no visible excretion, and almost no respiration. They mature during the winter and break out in the spring as adult moths.

**The juvenile hormone.** You may have wondered what makes the moth change from a tree-climbing caterpillar to a pupa and then to a colorful, flying adult. The British biologist, V. B. Wigglesworth, suggested the answer in the 1930s when he experimented, not with moths, but with a blood-sucking bug named Rhodnius. He decapitated the larvae, and, instead of dying, they were transformed into midget-sized adults. Further investigations convinced Wigglesworth that his little bloodsuckers were the result of missing *corpora allata,* two tiny glands projecting backward from each animal's brain. The glands secrete a

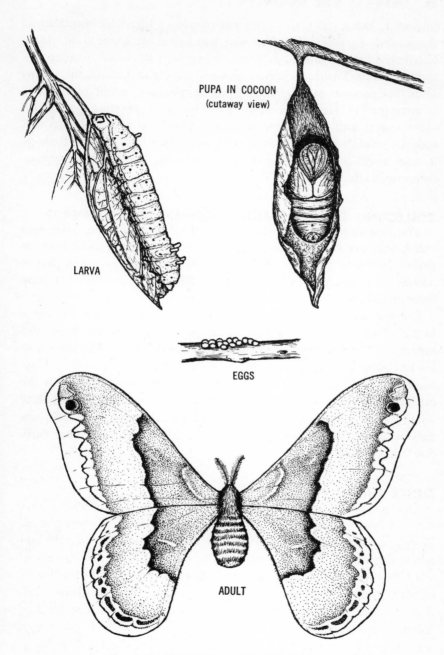

LARVA

PUPA IN COCOON
(cutaway view)

EGGS

ADULT

Fig. 8–1 LIFE CYCLE OF THE PROMETHEA MOTH

substance, influencing molts and emergences, which has been named the *juvenile hormone*. This hormone was found by others to be widely distributed among insects. A Frenchman, Jean Bounhiol, watched its action on the silkworm. When he removed the corpora allata, the worms spun tiny cocoons and later emerged as miniature adult moths. But he went further. He placed a number of hormone-secreting glands into older worms and from these got giant adults. Today, biologists still seek the juvenile hormone, often in animals other than insects. Perhaps in man it will alter the aging of tissues or have some other, as yet, undetermined effect.

## COLLECTING COCOONS AND WATCHING MOTHS EMERGE

The best time to find cocoons is in the fall or winter, after trees and bushes are bare of leaves. Look for them hanging from trees or among leaves on the ground. Remove the specimens to a box placed outside your window, or if part of the winter has passed, they may be brought inside.

Cut an oval window in one of your cocoons to observe the pupa inside (Fig. 8–1). Look for its future wings, mouthparts, eyes, and antennae. Their outlines will be seen without difficulty. The pupa will later become a normal adult unless you damaged it while cutting. Tape the oval "lid" back over the opening and hang this cocoon with the others in such positions that the adults will have room to unfold their wings when they emerge. With continued attention and good luck, you may witness this warm-weather event, which sometimes comes early due to heat of a house.

## OTHER THINGS TO DO

One phase or another of the moth life cycle is current throughout the year, and you may have opportunities to observe all of these phases. Watch for caterpillars in the late spring and early summer months and adults during the late summer. The larvae are especially instructive since they spin cocoons. Collect a few. Keep them well fed upon leaves of the type trees from which they were obtained. Observe them when they commence their complicated art of cocoon making. The brightly colored butterflies also deserve attention and so do their pupae which are usually called *chrysalides*. You may see these naked chrysalides hanging from branches or fence posts or find them under leaves. They remind one of moth pupae from which the cocoons are removed, but usually they show more color. These, too, may be collected and follow-up studies made of their life cycles.

Take a paintbrush and wipe a few of the tiny, powdery, overlapping scales off the wings of some of your moths and butterflies. Put these on a slide under a microscope. You will see a variety of colors and scale shapes as you examine the different species. Most of these colors derive from wastes of the developing pupae.

# 9
# SOCIAL LIFE IN AN ANT COLONY

**Materials.**
1. An ant's nest, containing queen(s) and workers (plus males, eggs, larvae, and pupae when available)
2. Observation nest, ordered or made from two $6'' \times 12''$ glass panes plus wood
3. Trowel or shovel and collecting jars

**Which are the social insects?** The honeybee, upon returning from her recent jaunt to a rich clover field, performs a dance which would put Arthur Murray to shame. With unexcelled vigor she circles about, first in one direction and then another. In the darkness of the hive, fellow workers excitedly join in. If the field is distant, the leader wags her tail and makes short dashes in a straight line indicating the direction. Soon many workers take off, shortly to alight in pollen-laden clover.

The *bee* would appear to be a distinctly clever creature, what with dancing, hive building, and association for the common good. Other insects, *wasps, ants,* and *termites,* also live and work together in a magnificent manner. As scientists, we usually attribute such insect social behavior to "automatic responses" and "instincts," but still we must wonder. Their brains are large for insects and their performances are certainly beyond the ordinary.

**The army ant's path of destruction.** In the tropics, the company of pursuing birds first calls one's attention to a moving *army* of *ants* several yards wide and sometimes hundreds of yards long, blackening the ground. The density of ants at the center forces many to the sides, where they swarm ahead in flanking movements. Confused and frightened insects are thereby flushed into the main body of ants, where they are quickly torn in pieces and carried off at the rear. Nothing escapes. Even horses that are left tied are eaten. Locusts and grasshoppers in flight are caught by the birds.

Many insects take to bushes or trees—a fatal mistake. Soon the ants come up, following every branch to its end, the bitter end for those preyed upon. With attackers close at hand, insects leap away, usually landing in troops below, there to be destroyed. Some spiders escape, however, by lowering themselves from limbs on their narrow silken threads.

Army ants have no permanent home. They do take intermittent rests when the larvae change to non-food-consuming pupae, at which time the queen also lays eggs. Temporary habitations for these purposes are made in hollow logs or trees, where the ants cluster about their queens in dense multitudes, numbering tens or hundreds of thousands. The group forms living passageways through which food is carried to the center, brought in by small raiding parties.

Army ants seem both wonderfully intelligent and amazingly ignorant. They march in an instinctively disciplined manner, rescue fellow ants in distress, make living bridges across difficult terrain, and generally show a high degree of social order. Yet, their unalterable marching behavior is sometimes their undoing. If once started in a circular path on flat ground, each ant continues to follow the comrade immediately in front until all perish from lack of water.

**Agricultural civilizations.** Solomon wrote, "Go to the ant, sluggard . . . and be wise . . . she prepares her food in summer, and gathers her sustenance in harvest." The ants referred to are *harvest ants,* various species of which are found in warm, dry regions. They husk and store seeds in chambers beneath the soil. Harvest ants actually do no planting, but there are other species which do, the fungus growers.

*Fungus growers* fertilize, weed, and guard their specialty with a mother's loving care. The queen starts the original garden by carrying small quantities of fungus to the new nest. Daughters, some only one hundredth her size, attend it later. The tiny ones weed out mold and contaminants, while larger workers gather leaves used as fertilizer.

**Cattle herds and honey ants.** Six-legged "cows" are collected in herds and milked by several species of ants. The cows are aphids or mealy bugs or other small insects. Their milk is a secretion of honeydew obtained when ants stroke the cows' backs with their antennae (feelers). The *dairying ants* collect eggs of aphids and take them to their own nests. Here they are carefully tended and, when hatched, they are placed on suitable plants, corn being especially exploited (Fig. 9–1). The aphids partially digest the sap of corn and pass a large part of this on to their masters.

A rather unusual system of honeydew storage is used by ants in desert regions where the supply is seasonal. Worker ants regurgitate the sweet liquid into the mouths of a select few. The abdomens of these few swell until they are spherical and tissue thin. Unable to move, they merely hang from the ceilings of specially constructed chambers. In time of need, these animated honey bags discharge sweets to their associates.

Fig. 9–1 WORKER ANT CARRYING APHID

**The typical ant society.** On a warm, humid, summer afternoon you may happen upon the craziest mess of ants you have ever seen. In your yard and in the yards of all your neighbors are thousands and thousands and thousands of ants running about in total confusion. This is the time of *swarming* and mating. Not only the usual *workers* but also many winged individuals are present. The large ones are new *queens;* the numberless smaller ants are *males.* After a few hours of disorder, the queens and their suitors take to flight and mate in the air.

Male ants perish a few days after the marriage, but the fertile queen lands, disposes of her wings, and tunnels into the ground (Fig. 9–2).

Fig. 9–2 WINGLESS QUEEN

Sealed from the outer world, her majesty waits alone patiently till her eggs mature. Curiously enough, her only nutriment at this time is obtained from the decomposition of flight muscles, no longer needed.

Ant *eggs* pass through *larval* and *pupal* stages before *adulthood* (Fig. 9–3). The larvae hatching from the first batch of eggs are fed a salivary secretion from the queen's royal mouth. The larvae sometimes spin cocoons and sometimes do not, depending upon the ant involved. Small workers emerging from this pupal state dig to the surface where they find food and bring it back to the queen and their developing sisters.

Fig. 9–3 EGG, LARVA, PUPA, AND ADULT

Her majesty's sole duty becomes that of laying eggs during the dozen or so remaining years of her life. Workers nurse the young, placing them in areas of proper warmth and moisture, licking larval secretions which they find pleasantly tasteful, and aiding the new workers in getting out of their cocoons. Other workers obtain plant or insect food upon which the colony feasts by regurgitating the partially digested material from one ant to another.

## COLLECTION AND STUDY OF ANTS

Select an ant nest, such as the common black or red ants of your own yard, and dig deep with a trowel or shovel around its main opening and to each side. Spread the dirt on the ground, or better, an old bed sheet, seeking first the queen(s). These are elusive, but with effort you should sooner or later find one. Place workers, winged males, and young (or whatever is available) in one jar, and the large queen in another. Both jars should contain dirt to be used in the artificial nest and to prevent drying.

Upon return to the laboratory, place the ants with earth in an insect observation nest such as those available from biological supply houses listed in Appendix E. If desired, the nest can be constructed from two panes of glass and a tight-fitting wooden frame (Fig. 9–4). Dampen the soil of the chamber at weekly intervals (but not so wet as to cause mold to develop). Honey plus an occasional soft-bellied insect or table scraps may be used for food. Only small quantities should be given.

Without undue disturbance, observe the ants as they construct their nest. Notice the use of legs and mouthparts in excavation. What is the reaction of workers in the presence of royalty? Introduce one or two strange ants and see the distress which this causes. What weapons are

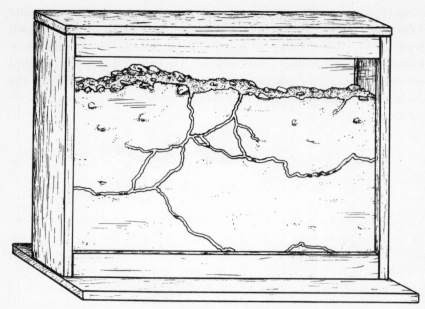

Fig. 9–4 ANT NEST

used for fighting? If not killed, the new individuals acquire the nest odor in a few hours and will then be accepted as fellow workers. The regurgitation of food from ant to ant is an important part of colony life. Watch for this transferral of nutrients. Place the ants in colder air and notice how their movements slow. Revive certain ones by blowing upon them with your hot, carbon-dioxide enriched breath.

## OTHER THINGS TO DO

Continue your studies by reading O. W. Richards, *The Social Insects,* Philosophical Library, New York, 1953, and the informative little book by Karl von Frisch, *Bees: Their Vision, Chemical Senses, and Language,* Cornell University Press, Ithaca, 1950. Von Frisch describes, in easily understood language, many experiments suitable for amateur biologists.

In the spring or summer while walking through a woods, take time to examine some of the old, dead tree stumps and logs. Perhaps you will find a colony of white-bodied termites. Look for the different castes, soldiers and workers being most common, then cut into the log to study the tunnels. Collect specimens and bring these to your laboratory in a jar with moist wood for food. Cut off the abdomen of one of the termites. Push out the intestine and tease it apart in a drop of saline solution on a slide. Under the microscope, look for the protozoa which enable termites to digest solid wood. For more experiments with social insects and other animals, look in C. P. Hickman, *A Field Manual of Animal Ecology and Natural History*, Burgess Publishing Company, Minneapolis, 1955.

# 10

# INHERITANCE AND THE FRUIT FLY

**Materials.**
1. Wild and vestigal-wing fruit fly stocks
2. Half-pint cream bottles or similar containers
3. Culture (growth) medium containing Cream of Wheat, molasses or Karo sirup, water, and powdered yeast
4. Ether and cotton
5. Hand lens

**"Improving" animals and plants.** Since cavemen first raised orphan cubs and tamed wild oats by spreading seeds in their fields, humans have tried to improve on nature. For ages, this was a matter of chance guided by witch doctor's incantations. Animal breeders noticed, however, the old "like father, like son" similarities and began selecting superior stock as parents. Still, many rules of *genetics,* the study of inherited characteristics, were ignored.

Today we are making tremendous advances. For instance, since 1940 the feed required to raise a three-pound broiler hen has dropped from twelve to seven pounds. Careful scientific selection of parents gives us more eggs, more milk, and more meat, at less cost than ever before. In plants, breeders have derived choice hybrid corns, and have combined rust (a fungus) resistance with frost resistance in wheat. Such improvements are indirectly (and sometimes directly) the result of persistent studies by a vegetable-growing monk of the mid-nineteenth century. His name was Gregor Mendel and with this a story begins.

**From peas to genetics.** Mendel was a favorite of his pupils at the high school in Austria. They liked his friendly, informal approach. As a priest he was highly respected among fellow monks, but authorities of natural science ignored him. Little did they know that Mendel's laws would someday become the backbone of genetics and that Mendel himself would achieve fame comparable to his contemporary, the evolutionist, Darwin.

In the monastery garden Mendel took over a small space and started growing peas, common edible peas. He differed from other breeders of the 1850s who worked for vast changes in whole organisms. Mendel investigated small, isolated aspects of heredity. He tested characters such as: (1) the seeds, whether round or wrinkled, (2) unripe pods, whether yellow or green, (3) the plants themselves, whether tall or small. These distinct characters are now known to be transmitted by *genes,* thousands of which make up *chromosomes* in individual animal and plant reproductive cells.

Mendel carefully removed pollen of round pea plants to the pistil (the center part of the flower which conducts pollen to the unfertilized seed) of wrinkled pea plants and patiently awaited as the progeny grew. Surprisingly, he found that this *first filial* ($F_1$ or "children") generation consisted entirely of round peas. Roundness then is a *dominant* unit of heredity as compared with wrinkled, which we call *recessive*. Again Mendel transferred pollen, but this time he used only $F_1$ plants, those which had both dominant and recessive genes. From hundreds of such crosses he came up with a very consistent ratio of three round seeds to one wrinkled. The wrinkled grandparents skipped the first generation only to deposit their characteristic in this *second filial* ($F_2$) generation.

Mendel continued experimenting with other characters and other generations. He showed that tall is dominant to short and that unripe green pods are dominant over yellow pods. He showed that two recessive parents (as wrinkled to wrinkled) beget only recessive (wrinkled) offspring. Mendel and his successors have furnished invaluable rules for plant and animal breeders and for those who predict the onset and course of inheritable diseases. We owe many thanks to this simple, inquisitive monk, the founder of genetics.

**Mutations.** Mendel's discovery of inheritable characteristics has been employed to explain evolution, but it has limits. Only those traits already existent in plants and animals can be transmitted. To bring about truly distinct changes one needs a *mutation,* a rare inheritable alteration of genes in reproductive cells. The accumulation of useful mutations over millions of years has allowed hands to develop from paws, and brains to develop from nerves. But not all mutations are beneficial. In man, for example, they are the original source of hemophilia, a disease in which blood will not clot. In fruit flies, mutations have produced some animals with flightless, vestigial (very small) wings. Since organisms have already evolved to near perfection, any accidental change in their structure or function will probably be for the worse.

**Why fruit flies?** The tiny, eighth-of-an-inch-long brown flies often found near ripened and rotting fruit are appropriately named fruit flies, or, as the geneticists prefer, *drosophila*. Very early in hereditary studies they were found to be a superior source of information. Because of size, dozens or hundreds can be kept in a single, half-pint cream bottle. This permits experimentation with the large numbers always required to validate genetic principles. Another advantage is their short reproductive cycle. Each generation grows from egg to reproductive maturity within ten to twelve days. This eliminates the months or years of waiting necessary in other animals to observe the results of a particular mating.

## PROCURING AND FEEDING FLIES

Fruit flies may be purchased from Burdick's Drosophila Supply or other biology houses mentioned in Appendix E. Special kits containing growth medium and an ether anesthetizer are likewise available. If you wish to prepare your own medium, a molasses-Cream of Wheat mixture is easy to fix, yet solid enough that flies may be shaken from their bottles. For this you will use 11.5 milliliters of molasses or Karo (one tablespoon), 77.5 milliliters of water (one-third cup), and 10.3 grams (one level tablespoon) of Cream of Wheat.* Add about two thirds of the water to the molasses and bring to the boiling point. Now pour in Cream of Wheat which has been mixed with the remaining third of cold water. Cook and stir for about five minutes, then pour into a half-pint cream bottle or other small bottle which has been sterilized by boiling. Just before putting in the flies, sprinkle the medium with dried powdered yeast. Add a piece of paper toweling so that the flies and larvae will have something to crawl on. Use a freshly made medium for each generation. This retards mold growth.

**Anesthetizing flies.** Flies should be anesthetized to unconsciousness for convenience in handling or sorting. A handy ether anesthetizer may be made from the same type bottle in which the flies are raised or from one which has the same size opening. Plug this bottle with cotton or a cork to which cotton has been nailed and tied. When ready to sort flies, put several drops of ether on the cotton plug and set the plug to one side. Now tap the other (fly culture) bottle, making the

---

* These quantities are sufficient for one half-pint cream bottle. Double or triple the recipe as required.

flies fall to the bottom. Quickly remove the lid and place your culture bottle mouth to mouth with the etherizer bottle. Turn the culture bottle upside down and tap, causing flies to fall into the etherizer, which should be plugged at once with ether-soaked cotton. In about fifteen seconds the flies will be motionless. Shake them out on a white card to sort males from females and mutant winged flies from the normal wild type. A knife blade is helpful for these separations.

And now a word of caution—fruit flies should be removed from ether soon after they fall unconscious or else they turn up their wings and die. On the other hand, they recover from ether in a few minutes. Sorting must be done rapidly. A little practice will temper your anesthetizing judgment.

**What to do when your flies come.** Examine the vials or bottles of drosophila as soon as they arrive, noting particularly the different life phases and sexes. Fruit flies have a life cycle similar to moths and ants, consisting of egg, larva, pupa, and adult. Use a hand lens and refer to Fig. 10–1. Find as many stages as possible. Wiggling larvae and non-motile pupae, as well as adults, are easily seen, but the tiny, white-colored eggs are almost invisible unless removed from their bottles. Differentiate males from females. Male flies are smaller and are blackened around the tail region. Females have pointed abdomens. Compare drosophila of the ordinary, long-winged wild-type stock with those having vestigial wings. Vestigial wings are small and wrinkled, causing their possessors to remain permanently grounded.

Transfer the supplier's flies (or larvae and pupae) to your own bottles of growth media. If desired, the vestigial and wild types may be kept in separate bottles for a couple of weeks. They mate and a new generation of flies appears, identical with their parents. Any number of such generations breed true unless a mutation occurs. This is very unlikely. The rate of gene mutations varies but is on the order of one in one million.

**Mating short- with long-winged drosophila.** Now you may test Mendel's ratios, those which demonstrate that heredity is directed by specific units (genes) and not by simple "blending of bloods." You must start by using only virgin females, a bit of a problem since flies start mating ten to twelve hours after birth. To do this, first clear your bottles of adult flies, saving only the eggs, larvae, and pupae. During the period of two to ten hours after the pupae commence hatching, separate adult males from females. By this means the females remain unfertilized.

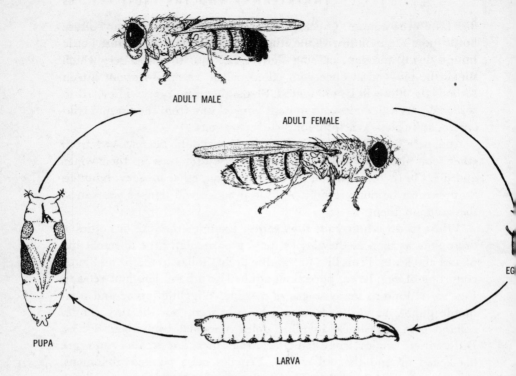

ADULT MALE

ADULT FEMALE

EG

PUPA

LARVA

Fig. 10-1 LIFE CYCLE OF THE FRUIT FLY

Mate virgin, vestigial-winged females with wild males by placing three or four pairs in each of two or three bottles. Label the bottle caps with the date and type of mating. In about a week remove the parents to prevent them from being confused with the offspring. Eggs become larvae in less than one day. Larvae molt twice and become pupae in eight days. Pupae become adults a few days later, a complete life cycle in less than two weeks. Examine these offspring, the $F_1$ generation (Fig. 10-2). There's not a single short-winged fly in the bunch! All are a wild type like their fathers. We see from this that wild is dominant and vestigial is recessive.

Put several $F_1$ pairs in two or three fresh bottles and label. Virgins need not be used in this cross, since all $F_1$ flies have the same genetic constitution. Each carries one dominant and one recessive gene from its parents. Remove the parents after one week, during which time they have mated and laid eggs. A few days later the F₂ flies start hatching, and this time there are some vestigials. Short wings skip one generation, but the recessive gene is still present. Etherize and separate flies into two classes—wild and vestigial. What is your ratio? Does it approximate Mendel's 3 : 1 ratio in peas?

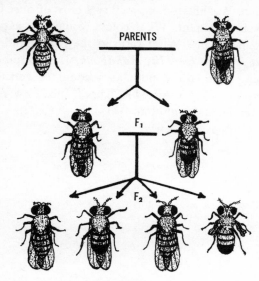

Fig. 10–2 MATING OF WILD TYPE AND VESTIGIAL FLIES

## OTHER THINGS TO DO

There are a large number of drosophila stocks available for investigating principles of heredity. To observe shelves of a genetics laboratory is an education in itself. Among more distinctive varieties are those having curved wings or black bodies or white eyes or almost no eyes at all. Wild type is dominant over each of these particular traits, and any of these stocks may be substituted for vestigial wings in the preceding experiment.

As a further test you might try this, if you like surprise endings. Mate ebony (dark black)-bodied flies with those having vestigial wings, but don't expect the children to look like their parents. From this cross you get only wild-type flies with ordinary brown bodies and long wings! Since both of these characters are dominant, they cover genes for black and vestigial. Now mate these F₁'s to bring out recessives. Their offspring (F₂'s) will appear in the following ratio: nine wilds to three vestigials to three black bodies to one fly having a black body and vestigial wings.

This is just the beginning if you are interested in genetics. Think up more of your own combinations or choose from those suggested in the pamphlet by M. Domereo and B. P. Kaufmann, *Drosophila Guide,* Carnegie Institution, Washington, 1950. Try a cross of pure black with white mice. Black is dominant. What colors would you expect in the first and second generations? What ratio in the grandchildren? Read A. Scheinfeld, *The Human Heredity Handbook,* J. B. Lippincott Company, Philadelphia, 1956, for a popular account of genetics, or R. Moore, *Man, Time, and Fossils,* Alfred A. Knopf, Inc., New York, 1953, for stories about Mendel and evolution.

# Animals with Backbones

---

## I I

## FISH AND AQUARIA

**Materials.**
1. An aquarium tank
2. Suitable native or tropical fish
3. Plants and coarse sand
4. Snails
5. A larger fish for dissection

**Oceans of fish.** An endless reservoir of food and animal life is contained in the world's great oceans. The area of the sea is three times that of land. Within these depths are foods never eaten by man and animals yet to be seen.

Of the edible fish, herring has been the most important. This is a North Atlantic animal especially numerous north of Cape Cod. In the fall, herring swim toward shore where they spawn (lay eggs). Maine canneries pack the small fry as sardines. Pacific canneries use pilchards, another member of the herring family, for the same purpose. Other noteworthy fish in the commercial catch are shad, cod, sturgeon (a source of caviar), salmon, tuna, haddock, mackerel, and menhaden. The last-named animal is a significant source of oil for the chemical industries.

Fish have striking adaptations for sea life. Most are slim and stream-lined for swimming. Bottom movers, however, are flattened and may have both eyes on one side of the head. Sawfish have a murderous sawlike head extension for slashing their prey. Rays sometimes possess potent stinging tails. Flying fish glide above water to avoid underwater enemies. Most unusual of all are the grotesque forms living in the ocean's darkened depths. Their bodies are adapted to withstand exceptionally high pressures, and many have luminous organs to light their way.

**Fresh-water sport.** The most popular recreation in America requires only a pole, a line, and a hook. The barefoot boy with his can of worms may have equal or better luck than the adult with the finest of tackle. Fish prefer worms, minnows, and insects, but will bite at almost anything from green stamps to ivory soap.

Among more desirable food and game fish are trout, bass, pike, sunfish, perch, and catfish. Trout and pike prefer cold northern or mountain lakes and streams. The catfish, although known in the north, is better exploited in the warm, muddy waters of Dixie, where its meat is highly prized. Various species of bass, sunfish, and perch are widely distributed in North America and just as widely fished for.

**Kinds of fish.** There are two classes of fish: (1) those with a cartilaginous skeleton, such as *sharks* and *rays,* and (2) fish having a bony skeleton (Fig. 11–1). The vast majority of all fresh-water and marine fishes have bony skeletons.

Sharks are very primitive animals, many with evil reputations. The rare whale shark is the largest of all, fifty feet in length. Hammerheads have flattened extensions of the head on which eyes are located. The tiger shark is a streamlined fish of warm surface waters. Some sharks make good eating.

Rays are unusually well adapted for a sea-bottom existence. Their forwardly placed (pectoral) fins are very large, compared with those of ordinary fish. By flapping these, they glide about. Both eyes are located at the top of the head, while mouth and gills are found on the undersurface.

Fishes having bony skeletons include all the forms previously mentioned, with the exception of sharks and rays. Gills are covered by a single flap (the operculum) on each side, as opposed to several external openings in sharks and rays.

**Fish anatomy.** Next time you go fishing, do a little more than just eat your catch. Take time to examine the outside, then remove the insides piece by piece. Study the surface first (Fig. 11–2). There are only two sets of paired fins: *pectoral* fins just behind the gills and *ventral* fins on the underside. Three hundred million years ago fins evolved into the limbs of land animals. Had there been more than two pairs, higher animals might now have six or eight arms and legs. *Spiny dorsal* and *soft dorsal* fins are located on the back. The soft

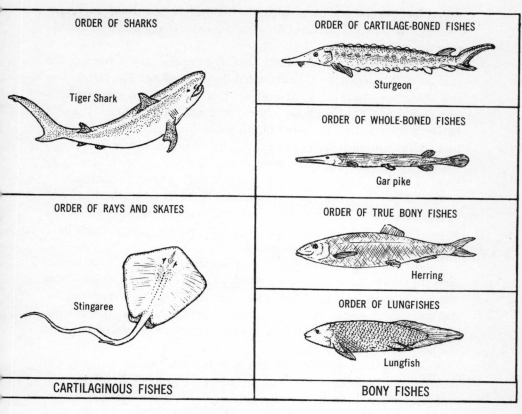

| CARTILAGINOUS FISHES | BONY FISHES |

ORDER OF SHARKS

Tiger Shark

ORDER OF RAYS AND SKATES

Stingaree

ORDER OF CARTILAGE-BONED FISHES

Sturgeon

ORDER OF WHOLE-BONED FISHES

Gar pike

ORDER OF TRUE BONY FISHES

Herring

ORDER OF LUNGFISHES

Lungfish

Fig. 11–1 THE ORDERS OF FISHES

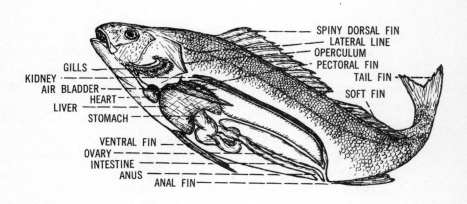

SPINY DORSAL FIN
LATERAL LINE
OPERCULUM
PECTORAL FIN
TAIL FIN
SOFT FIN

GILLS
KIDNEY
AIR BLADDER
HEART
LIVER
STOMACH

VENTRAL FIN
OVARY
INTESTINE
ANUS
ANAL FIN

Fig. 11–2 ANATOMY OF A PERCH

dorsal fin is nearer the tail, which has itself developed a fin, important for steering and locomotion. An *anal* fin is located on the underside near the tail.

Fish obtain oxygen from water flowing over the gills. Covering the gills on each side is a hard plate called the *operculum*. The *lateral line* is a lighter area running along both sides of the fish body from operculum to tail fin. This is a sense organ for detecting vibrations. Even in perfectly dark water fish do not bump into rocks, thanks to their lateral lines. Most fish have scales of varying shapes which aid in identifying the species. Fish scales often show annual rings of growth similar to those of a tree. There is less scale growth during winter months.

While opening a fish, note the location of the heart at the head end beneath the gills. If the fish has been recently killed, the *two-chambered heart* will still be beating. Mammals (including man) and birds have a more efficient heart with four chambers.

Follow from the mouth the tube leading into the *stomach*. Continuous with the stomach is the *intestine,* which absorbs food and carries wastes on out through the *anus*. The anus is located near the front edge of the anal fin. A second opening between the anus and fin passes from the *ovary* of a female or *testis* of a male. The *liver* is located between the heart and stomach.

Near the backbone one will find a swim or *air bladder*. Gases obtained from the fish's blood fill this bladder when he desires to ascend. In some species it can be used for gulping in breaths of fresh air at the water surface. On the back side of the swim bladder are the long dark *kidneys*.

## THE AQUARIUM (Fig. 11–3).

Over 20,000,000 people in the United States are addicted to the aquarium habit, and with good reason. Where can you find quieter or less troublesome pets. Their simple, subtle beauty adorns many city apartments in which other creatures would quickly fail or be thrown out by the landlord.

A suitable tank for fish should be large, preferably of five gallons or greater capacity, but settle for less if your pocketbook does not permit extravagance. Select hardier varieties of fish for small aquaria (ask your dealer). The water temperature fluctuates more and, of course, the capacity for fish and plants is reduced.

Thoroughly wash sufficient sand to cover the bottom of your tank to a one-inch depth. Add the sand and pour in water nearly to fill the tank. Pond water is preferred. If not available, use tap water which has been in an open container for three or four days.

Plants should be added to increase the attractiveness of your aquarium. They also provide shelter, some food, and attachment for eggs. Recommended vegetation includes Vallisneria, Sagittaria, Myriophyllum, Cabomba, and Anacharis. Aquarium-grown plants are better adapted and more enduring than pond plants.

Locate the aquarium in strong diffused light if possible. Do not expose to sunlight for more than one to two hours daily. Add fish and a few snails after the water has cleared and plants have started to grow. Snails act as scavengers, cleaning up uneaten food. A glass-plate cover for the tank will prevent your fish from jumping out.

Fig. 11–3 THE AQUARIUM WITH A SHINER AND SAGITTARIA ON THE LEFT, A DARTER AND CABOMBA ON THE RIGHT

**Fish for aquaria.** Native species will probably provide the most entertainment. Small fish can be seined without difficulty. Try to procure a few red-bellied daces, a good aquarium fish and very colorful. Include some of the more common shiners and minnows. Look also for darters and killifish. Pictures and descriptions of these and other familiar species will be found in H. S. Zim and H. H. Shoemaker, *Fishes,* Simon and Schuster, New York, 1956. Imported fish may be preferred for a second aquarium. Of these there is infinite variety. Guppies are recommended as good, inexpensive fish for beginners. Platies, white cloud mountain fish, angelfish, and gouramis are also favored.

Never overcrowd fish nor put them in a container with a small exposed water surface. Under these conditions, carbon dioxide may accumulate to stifling proportions. In the usual rectangular tanks one or two inches of fish in a gallon of water is considered safe. Food requirements vary with different species. Usually a well-balanced prepared food is satisfactory. Do not overfeed. Supplement occasionally with living insects or Daphnia, a very small crustacean.

## OTHER THINGS TO DO

You may fill your aquarium with creatures other than fish. Seine a pond or lake and see what you come up with. Probably you will find water insects of many varieties, perhaps including the giant water bug, the male of which carries the female's eggs on his back. Tadpoles and aquatic salamanders may also be in your catch. Each animal will provide many hours of pleasurable observation. Any insects you catch may be mounted and added to your collection as described in Chapter 7.

In clear water, swim among the fish and make direct observations. Use a glass-covered mask for best vision. If you have or can secure the equipment, try skin-diving.

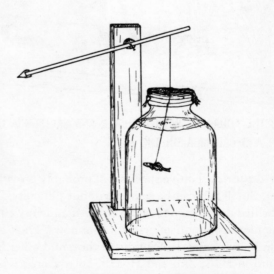

Fig. 11–4 APPARATUS FOR MEASURING FISH MOVEMENTS

Fish make good subjects for physiological studies, since their movements are readily recorded. Tie a thread securely around the body of a fish two inches or greater in length, or pull a threaded needle beneath its dorsal fin. Mount a piece of screen wire above your aquarium or some similar container. Attach the tied thread through an opening in the wire to one end of a soda straw lever (Fig. 11–4). Make the lever by sticking a pin through a straw into a cork mounted on a ring stand. Motion is transmitted to the straw which swings up and down. Scientists use this device to demonstrate effects of drugs such as tranquilizers (Miltown, chlorpromazine, etc.). These produce inactivity and even halt the belligerence of male Siamese fighting fish. The effects of stale and oxygenated water can be similarly shown. Permanent records may be made on rotating smoked kymograph drums, if your school happens to own one of these.

Some excellent reading material plus photographs of various fish are contained in G. Borgeson and L. Borgeson, *Home Aquarium Handbook,* Arco Publishing Company, Inc., New York, 1957. Discussions of photography and sea aquaria are among its chapters.

# 12

# TERRARIA FOR AMPHIBIANS AND REPTILES

### Materials.
1. One or more terraria
2. Amphibians, reptiles, and plants

**Introducing the amphibians.** A most curious creature is the African lungfish. In ages past this fish evolved lungs suitable for a prolonged stay on land. Lungfish easily survive brief droughts, but unfortunately the mutations (spontaneous changes) of the lungfish have not included a set of limbs. Locomotion is impossible and doom is probable during prolonged dry periods.

Another fish with unusual habits is the sea robin. Exceptionally well-developed fins enable him to crawl about in gulf mud, seeking crabs, worms, and mollusks. Can he survive on land? Not for long. The sea robin has no lungs.

Mutations are interesting things. If Nature had simply given the lungfish legs or the legged fish lungs, a new land animal would have been born. Has this ever happened? Certainly, and the date was 300,000,000 years ago. This was the period when amphibians first appeared.

What are amphibians? They are animals with double lives. As larvae they remain in water, breathing with gills as do fish. When sufficiently old, most larvae undergo a transition, or *metamorphosis*. They lose gills and gain lungs and limbs, enabling them to live on land. The tadpole's change into a frog is an example of such a metamorphosis.

There are three orders of living amphibians. The two common orders are the *salamanders* and a group containing *frogs* and *toads* (Fig. 12-1). A third order contains blindworms, a group of tropical animals.

**What are reptiles?** At first glance it appears there are few differences between an amphibian, such as the salamander, and a reptile, such as the lizard. Reptiles, however, are permanent land creatures. They never experience a larval stage with gills. The soft egg masses of amphibians are supplanted by shelled eggs. Some snakes and lizards

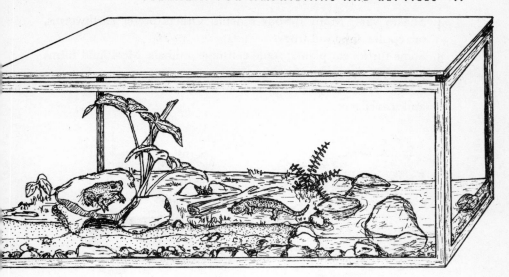

Fig. 12–1 SWAMP TERRARIUM FOR AMPHIBIANS

bear living young. Externally, reptiles are protected by horny scales or bony plates, while amphibians have a softer skin which is usually moist.

Although they were formerly the most important of all land animals, there are now only five surviving reptilian orders. In one of these, all members are extinct except the ancient-looking tuatara of New Zealand. The other and more common orders contain: (1) the lizards, (2) the snakes, (3) the turtles, and (4) the crocodiles and alligators (Fig. 12–2).

**Food selection.** During warm weather most amphibians and reptiles feed daily if there is an abundance of food. In captivity two or three feedings per week are generally adequate (one for snakes). Keep in mind that the cold body of these animals indicates a reduced energy and food requirement. At lower temperatures, some frogs survive an entire year without eating.  ˙

What nutrients are needed? Mostly living insects, but this varies. Generally speaking, the requirements are as follows:

1.  Aquatic salamanders like crayfish, fish, insects, and plants. Their land brothers eat insects and spiders.
2.  Frogs and toads eat insects, spiders, and small worms. Tadpoles are mostly vegetarian, eating moss or decayed plants.
3.  Lizards feed mainly on insects.

4. Snakes vary. Many devour rodents. Others prefer earthworms, or reptiles, fish, and frogs.
5. Some turtles eat plants; some consume animals. Most land forms are vegetarians.
6. Alligators like crayfish, fish, and insects. Crocodiles are meat-eaters and scavengers.

HORNED LIZARD       RIBBON SNAKE

SLIDER TURTLE       ALLIGATOR

Fig. 12–2 REPRESENTATIVES OF FOUR ORDERS OF REPTILES

Food is normally taken only at a temperature in which amphibians and reptiles are comfortable and active. Digestion is most rapid in a warm environment. Non-feeding reptiles can sometimes be induced to feed simply by heating their cages.

**The proper environment.** Amphibians and reptiles are often mentioned as "cold-blooded" animals, but this does not mean that they are always cold. Their body temperatures vary with that of their surroundings. They heat up considerably while sunning on warm rocks or in other similar situations.

Excessively hot or cold environments are not well tolerated. For this reason they burrow into the ground or beneath logs in extremes of temperature. This is especially true during the winter when almost all such creatures hibernate. In general, reptiles are active at higher temperatures than are amphibians.

Humidity is of considerable importance, especially to amphibians. They spend most of their time in or near a damp environment. Reptiles tolerate greater variations but usually prefer a somewhat humid location.

## COLLECTING AMPHIBIANS AND REPTILES

Amphibians and reptiles are shy. They conceal themselves under rocks, bark, and leaf litter. The insides of rotting logs also make good hide-outs. Take a walk in the woods and turn or roll over objects to find these animals.

For amphibians, a stout net of one-eighth-inch mesh cloth with a handle three to four feet in length will prove helpful. Seek them at swamps, lakes, or in other moist surroundings. Amphibians are more numerous just after a warm rain. Locate frogs and toads by their calls. Flash a light in their eyes, and they often remain stationary till caught. Try seining long-established ponds to get tadpoles and aquatic salamanders.

Lizards and snakes may be noosed. For small lizards use a wooden handle fitted with fish line or ✄40 sewing thread for a noose (Fig. 12–3). For snakes use a heavier leather noose. Snakes can also be pinned

Fig. 12–3 SNAKE NOOSE

down with the foot or a stick. Grab the animal just back of the head to avoid snakebite. Be familiar with and beware of poisonous species. Keep living specimens in jars or muslin bags till they can be brought to more adequate housing. Place dampened moss or leaf litter in these containers.

**Terraria, homes for captive animals.** A terrarium is a cage or tank in which live amphibians and reptiles are kept as pets. Requirements of individual animals vary. Most will come from either a swamp, woodland, or desert habitat and will feel at home in similar environments.

Permanent terraria should be large sized. A five- to ten-gallon container is ideal. For this purpose one may use an aquarium tank, battery jar, or other large observation chamber. One-gallon bottles may be used for short-term studies.

Cover the terrarium top with a glass plate, propped up slightly to allow entry of air. This prevents animals from escaping and maintains a higher humidity. Cages for snakes and desert animals should be covered with a tight-fitting screen wire lid.

Use both native animals and plants in terraria but do not overcrowd either. Include areas of seclusion such as rock overhangs or small hollow logs.

**The swamp terrarium.** Many amphibians and a few reptiles will do well in watery surroundings. Allow several inches of water at one end of the tank. Build the other end up slightly with rocks, sand, and a little soil. Add both land and water plants to complete the picture.

Amphibians suited for this semi-aquatic terrarium are turtles, tadpoles or frogs, newts, and aquatic salamanders. For reptiles you might select alligators and water snakes. Expose the alligators to some sunshine or other light and heat during the day.

**The woodland terrarium.** The foundation should consist of a bottom gravel layer, followed by layers of sand and soil. Fill with water to the base of the soil. Add woodland plants (mosses, ferns, liverworts) as desired. Sink a pan of drinking water into the soil. Most animals will drink from this, although some lizards will take water only from sprinkled plants. Snakes prefer a water dish that permits complete submersion. Put toads, tree frogs, woodland salamanders, lizards, or snakes in this terrarium.

**The desert terrarium.** Fill the tank with a few inches of sand on which have been placed two or three large rocks. Add cactus and a shallow pan of drinking water. Keep the lower level of sand moistened with a small amount of water.

Desert animals need warmth. This can be simply accomplished by suspending a light bulb over one end of the cage. The cage temperature should vary from 80 to 90°F. during the day to 70° at night.

Appropriate animals include the horned lizard (mistakenly called horned toad) and other desert lizards and snakes. If there are no deserts in your neighborhood, procure specimens from the living stocks of dealers listed in Appendix E.

## OTHER THINGS TO DO

Amphibians and reptiles generally lead secluded lives. This, combined with their relatively minor economic importance, has deterred many scientists from detailed studies. Amateurs sometimes make very worthwhile observations. Watch amphibians and reptiles both in the field and in terraria. Keep careful records of their habits, foods, and active periods.

A good field book is invaluable for proper identification of the numerous species. As a starter, you might try that of H. S. Zim and H. M. Smith, *Reptiles and Amphibians,* Simon and Schuster, Inc., New York, 1956. For more exacting, advanced work, choose R. Conant, *A Field Guide to Reptiles and Amphibians,* Houghton Mifflin Company, Boston, 1958.

# 13

# IDENTIFYING BIRDS

**Materials.**
1. Binoculars if available
2. Field guide on birds

**Food, feathers, and fertilizer.** In 1848 the Mormons of Utah were threatened with a disastrous cricket plague. Crops were a certain loss until thousands upon thousands of California gulls descended on the fields, saving the settlers from probable famine. The thankful Mormons erected a $40,000 monument to these birds and made the killing of gulls unlawful, subject to heavy penalties.

Insects are the chief food of many birds, and their appetites (despite notions to the contrary) are tremendous. A few eat fruit or grain, much to the distress of farmers. In weighing the good or bad of any bird, the over-all diet must be kept in mind. Most birds are beneficial when it comes to dollars-and-cents measurement.

As food and game, birds are certainly worth-while. What man will refuse "seconds" when the meal consists of fried chicken or roast duck. And the whir of bobwhite wings or the drum of a cock grouse are sounds which draw sportsmen like a Pied Piper's pipe.

On the subject of monetary value, we must mention feathers; those of egrets and herons once brought thirty-two dollars an ounce, almost the price of gold. Eider down and other similar downs are currently in demand as insulation for bedding.

Sometimes called the world's "most valuable bird" is the guanay cormorant, prized for its excrement. These birds land on islands off the coast of Peru and deposit a fertilizer which is exceptionally rich in phosphates and nitrogen. The immense numbers of cormorants cover the islands as thoroughly as a rainfall and so does their valuable product.

**Adaptation to flight.** What distinguishes birds from other animals? Usually wings, and always feathers. The light, durable feathers are an obvious asset to flight. Birds fly by drawing their wings rapidly downward against the air, with feathers held firmly together. Strength for wing movements is provided by unusually well-developed *pectoral muscles* in the breast. The breastbone (sternum) has adapted by enlarging to provide more surface attachment for the muscles. Another attribute of the bones is their exceptional light weight, resulting from a hollow, tubular type of structure.

An enormous amount of energy is required for flight. Birds, therefore, must consume much food and must breathe very effectively to bring in oxygen which converts food to energy. The lungs of birds have extensions, called *air sacs,* which pass into the abdomen and even into the hollow cavities of bones. Gas in the lungs and air sacs can be totally exhaled as opposed to only a partial emptying in man and other animals. The blood system is highly efficient in circulating oxygen derived from the lungs. Bird hearts have four chambers as do the hearts of mammals.

Birds depend on vision, and their eyes have developed remarkable abilities to distinguish between two objects which are very close to each other. The sparrow hawk, for example, has a visual acuity eight times that of man. Hearing also is acute in birds. In World War I, pheasants and many smaller birds became agitated by the sound of gunfire 2 16 miles distant.

**From egg to maturity.** When male birds arrive in the spring, they usually stake out a territory, singing loudly and frequently to proclaim their presence. The female arrives later, and, following courtship, the pair establish a nest.

Several eggs are ordinarily laid, and the female (or sometimes the male) sits upon them to keep them warm. Incubation is aided by the development of an *incubation patch,* a featherless area on the underside. Vessels of the skin in this area permit a warm blood supply to flow constantly near the eggs. Most birds do not remain indefinitely with the eggs; they take time off for feeding. Some of the more gentlemanly males bring food to their mates.

Newborn are sometimes bare or sometimes covered with down, depending on the species. They remain in the nest, expecting much attention from the parents. Feeding is accomplished by poking insects or worms far down their gaping mouths.

Young birds instinctively learn to fly and sing, but performance is often improved in the presence of their elders. The venture into flight is preceded by exercises of the wings and explorations of the area near the nest.

Parents and young usually accompany each other after leaving the nest. The young birds, however, quickly learn to shift for themselves. During the warm summer months there is less singing and activity, but with the advent of fall a remarkable journey is in store for most feathered animals.

**Migration.** Do they hear it? Do they feel it? What is the irresistible, irreplaceable call which draws birds southward as the days grow shorter? This problem has interested men since Aristotle (about 350 B.C.) noticed that robins disappear in fall while redstarts do not. He concluded that robins turn into redstarts.

Some light was thrown on the problem when, in migratory season, caged birds were observed assuming definite southward positions. Removal from sunlight caused disorientation. In artificial light the birds assumed varying positions, depending on the location of the light. Night flyers guide themselves by stars, as was disclosed in similar experiments, particularly by placing birds under the lighted dome of a planetarium.

Scientists are agreed now that light is important for bird navigation but are uncertain of the exact nature of stimulation. Reproductive glands are known to regress as the days grow shorter but grow markedly with increased light. These changes seem to be correlated with periods of migration.

Carrier pigeons and some other birds learn to home at distances up to and exceeding 1000 miles. Migrating birds travel one-way distances of up to 11,000 miles. Some are capable of pin-pointing their exact same nesting spot year after year. How their tiny brains enable them to navigate such enormous distances is a mystery which may long remain unsolved.

**Variety in birds.** The smallest birds in the world are *hummingbirds*. Some species are barely larger than a bumblebee and weigh less than a dime. Their wings are but a blur as they dash up and sip flower nectar through long, slender bills. Like helicopters, hummingbirds fly frontward or backward, up, down, and sideways, or remain motionless in the air. Their activity drops enormously at night when they are unable to see for feeding. In fact, they hibernate, becoming so inanimate that they consume only one fiftieth of the daytime oxygen requirement.

Not all birds bother with the problems of nest building and family raising. One example is the *cowbird,* a blackbird named for its habit of eating insects on and about cows. The mother lays her eggs in the nests of other birds and allows foster parents to incubate and baby-sit. The large, greedy cowbirds often starve out their baby brothers.

For real speed you can't beat *peregrine falcons* (duck hawks). In dives they acquire velocities of up to 200 miles per hour. Falcons have been trained to bring meat to their masters' tables for almost 3000 years. Hawks, eagles, and other birds of prey are sometimes similarly trained in the noble art of falconry.

Hikers in the mountains of western United States may see an ordinary-looking bird dive into a stream where it walks and flies about, looking for underwater insects. This is the *dipper,* a bird which cheerily persists in gathering food from river bottoms even when ice has formed on many parts of the surface.

Flightless birds are not too uncommon in many regions. Of especial note are *penguins* in Antarctica, *ostriches* in Africa, *kiwis* in New Zealand, and chickens. Standing eight feet tall, the ostrich is the world's largest bird.

## SEEING BIRDS

Facts alone are held in the emptiness of an unused encyclopedia. By studying real lives and real personalities, we get an honest acquaintance with our world, and we make friends. The man who observes birds and other animals is never alone. In his own back yard or on the most distant coasts of the world he is forever surrounded by living comrades.

When and where do you look and listen? The best season is spring. The bright-colored males are singing loudly and going about their business of territory defense and courtship. Different species are found in different locations, but generally the best places to look are in parks, at the edge of woods, and in marshlands. Binoculars are an asset to accurate observation.

On walks to and from school, around lakes, or on hikes through woods, identify as many birds as possible. The attempt may be made at any time of the year but yields greatest success in the early morning hours of spring or during fall migration. Start with robins, starlings, sparrows, and pigeons. Advance to flickers, warblers, herons, and hummingbirds. Notice not only differences of physical appearance (referring to Fig. 13–1 for marks of identification) but also variations of song and habit. Without disturbing the parents, locate nests with eggs and young birds (Fig. 13–2). When observed through binoculars these provide unusually good material for complete life studies. Identify unfamiliar eastern or central North American species in the book by R. T. Peterson, *A Field Guide to the Birds,* Houghton Mifflin Company, Boston, 1947. In western America use *A Field Guide to Western Birds* by the same author.

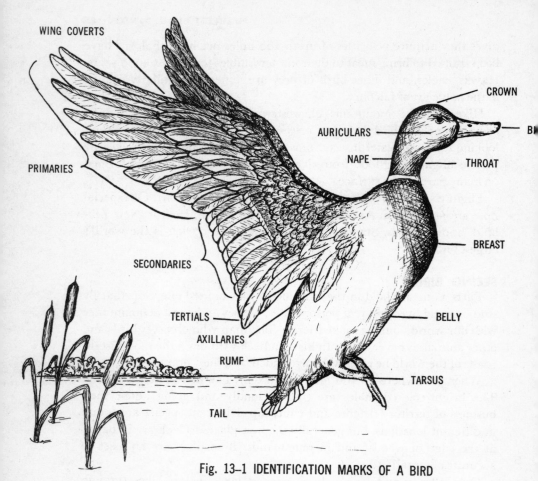

WING COVERTS

CROWN

AURICULARS

B

PRIMARIES

NAPE

THROAT

SECONDARIES

BREAST

TERTIALS

BELLY

AXILLARIES

RUMF

TARSUS

TAIL

Fig. 13–1 IDENTIFICATION MARKS OF A BIRD

Fig. 13–2 FIVE-HOUR-OLD KILLDEER

## OTHER THINGS TO DO

Construct nest boxes for wrens and martins and build feeding stations. Birds are easily attracted to stations in the winter, especially when snow is on the ground. Feeding provides a most humane method for disposal of bread crumbs and meat scraps. Provide seeds and grains for variety. Hummingbirds are sometimes lured into arm's reach by special feeders advertised in the *Audubon Magazine*.

Several good books have been written about birds. We suggest R. S. Lemmon, *Our Amazing Birds,* Doubleday & Company, Inc., Garden City, New York, 1952, or the somewhat more advanced G. J. Wallace, *An Introduction to Ornithology,* The Macmillan Company, New York, 1955.

# 14

# ON THE TRAIL OF MAMMALS

**Materials.**
  1. A one- or two-day-old snowfall or a muddy field

**Mammals of yesteryear.** Tiny warm-blooded mammals, evolving from lizards, were hardly noticed during the age of mighty dinosaurs. Yet, they were there, and as the millions of years rolled by, they became the dominant form of life. The testimony of fossils clearly shows elephants without trunks, dog-sized horses, hairy-skinned mammoths, and sabertoothed tigers. Primitive man made his first appearance almost one million years ago, leaving behind bones, tools, and cave art. Fossil evidence of men and other mammals is numerous, but so are the "missing links"; the field is wide open for young adventurers.

**What are mammals?** Newborn animals nursing—this is the peaceful scene which sets *mammals* apart from other warm-blooded, backboned animals. All mammals, from the tiniest of shrews to man and the largest whales, depend on a mother's milk. All mammals also have hair on their bodies during some phase of life. They usually are born alive and show a complex nervous system.

There are three divisions of the class called mammals: monotremes, marsupials, and placentals. *Monotremes* are primitive. They lay eggs and show other similarities to reptiles. The only living representatives are the duck-billed platypus and spiny anteater. *Marsupials* such as the kangaroo and opossum, are pouch-bearers. The young are born very small and scurry to the warmth of mother's pouch for further development. An entire litter of fifteen to eighteen newborn 'possums can be placed together in a single tablespoon. *Placental* mammals develop their young inside the body of the mother, attached to a nutrient membrane called the placenta. These include the vast majority of mammals— horses, cows, bats, cats, dogs, whales, monkeys, man, and so forth.

**Flying and echolocation in bats.** "Flying" lemurs or squirrels throw themselves from treetops and may glide fifty yards or more by spreading out parachutelike membranes between fore and hind limbs. Despite such performances, true aerial locomotion is found, among mammals, only in the bats. All bats fly, from the small mouselike forms commonly found in caves to the flying fox of India, some with wing-spreads of five feet.

Bats navigate and catch insects even in total darkness. They do this by emitting inaudible or nearly inaudible clicking sounds which strike objects and bounce back as an echo. Analysis of these sounds enables the bat accurately to judge size and distance.

**Whales, the champion breath holders.** Whales, manatees, and porpoises are underwater creatures, but they must breathe air as do all other mammals. Their breath holding capacities are enormous. Whales have been known to submerge for two full hours and are believed to dive 3000 feet down! The lungs of water mammals are small, but they almost totally fill with air during each inhalation. However, the real secret of prolonged breath holding is an amazing reduction of energy needs during submersion. Oxygen consumption occurs at only fifteen per cent of the normal rate. Heart rate also is diminished, reminding one of a similar condition in hibernation.

**The long winter sleep.** About the time of the first frost a well-rounded, fat-filled woodchuck retires to his cozy den. An inactive state develops and his body temperature drops to that of his surroundings, sometimes near the freezing point of water. In *hibernation* the wood-chuck's needs are almost negligible, so much so, in fact, that he eats no food; his breathing rate is sometimes less than once per minute, and his heart beats but a few times per minute. The woodchuck is only one of several mammals which hibernate to varying degrees. Ground squirrels and bats are equally idle in winter. Bears, skunks, and raccoons hole up, but do not show the extreme reductions of temperature and energy needs.

A "return of life" occurs with the warmer days of spring. Hibernators awake slowly; the body temperatures and breathing rates gradually return to normal. They then seek food to replace their loss of weight during the winter.

**Playing possum.** Camouflage is one of nature's favorite deceptions. A spotted fawn lying in a thicket dappled with sunlight is nearly invisible. Certain rabbits and foxes have snowy white hair in the winter but brown hair in the summer. Opossums (also shrews and moles) have another means of deceit. Overwhelming danger causes these animals to lie down, pretending death. Scientists believe that this is not a conscious act but a form of shock caused by fear—a faint instead of a feint.

**Survival on the desert.** Mammals have adapted to the air and the sea, but just as remarkable is their ability to survive on inhospitable land. They are found in the coldest and wettest of climates, and likewise in the hottest and driest. As an example of the latter, we shall consider the kangaroo rat, a hopping inhabitant of the deserts of the southwestern United States, whose diet consists of seeds and dry plants. The kangaroo rat is a total abstainer from water, yet sixty-five per cent of its body weight is water. Where does it come from? Laboratory studies have shown that even the cells of dry seeds are half water. Also, as in other animals, water is manufactured as a by-product of chemical reactions within the body. These small amounts are carefully conserved by the rat. Only a minimum of concentrated urine and dry feces are excreted. Sweat loss is negligible due to an almost complete lack of sweat glands. In addition, kangaroo rats remain underground by day, becoming active only at night. This is how they, and many similar desert animals, survive in a hostile, dry climate.

**The intellect of apes.** In working with monkeys or apes, experimenters comment that they often wonder who is testing whom. The curious creatures always seem to find the peepholes through which observers are watching and thereafter watch the observers.

Chimpanzees most nearly approach the mentality and emotional state of man. Each animal is an individual personality—friendly, antagonistic, or self-confident. Some sit alone in their corners; others like to get out with the gang. Almost all, but especially the youngsters, are playful and investigative.

Chimpanzees are said to show "insight" by reasoning that two sticks can be joined together to reach beyond the limits of one stick. They are quite as good as human children at solving certain problems, but fall far short on others. The inability to speak or count effectively inhibits their best performance.

**The significance of tracks and trails.** Lord Baden-Powell was one of the most remarkable men who ever lived. Most of us recall him as the founder of the Boy Scouts. He was also a British general and renowned spy, unsurpassed at following animal or human trails and making appropriate deductions. In fact, this was how he met his wife. Baden-Powell had learned to recognize character traits by the person's manner of walking. While in London one day he noticed the prints of a girl who "trod in a way that showed her to be possessed by honesty of purpose and common sense as well as the spirit of adventure." Two years later he noticed the same gait in a fellow passenger sailing for the West Indies. Upon introducing himself, he established that this was the correct lady and married her.

Civilized men forget the importance of tracks. Stalkers of the past (and a few in the present) knew that the trail led directly to their next meal. Naturalists of today recognize in tracks many clues to animal activity—how they hunt or are hunted, where they live, and so forth. A trail through the snow is sometimes the only record of a particular animal's existence in your locale.

## ON THE TRAIL

Select a day on which there is a recently fallen light snow, or, lacking snow, visit the sand and mud beaches of ponds and streams. Look for tracks in areas near woods and abandoned fields. Follow the trail as far as possible. Make life-sized sketches and identify by referring to the authoritative book of O. Murie, *A Field Guide to Animal Tracks,* Houghton Mifflin Company, Boston, 1954, or that of the well-known naturalist, E. T. Seton, *Animal Tracks and Hunter Signs,* Doubleday & Company, Inc., Garden City, New York, 1958. Note by the distance between tracks whether the animal was moving slowly or rapidly. The prints of swift runners are spread far apart.

Two of the most frequently seen and easily recognized trails are those of the cottontail rabbit and squirrel (Figs. 14–1 and 14–2). Both

Fig. 14–1 RABBIT TRAIL

animals move by leaps. Their hind feet fall in front of the forefeet. The hind feet of a squirrel point slightly outward. Toes and even toenails of the latter may be visible in fresh snow.

There also are lessons to learn while following domesticated animals. Take your pet(s) for a walk through snow or mud. Observe that dogs and cats leave distinctly different trails when walking as compared

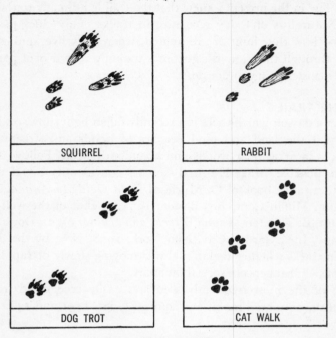

Fig. 14–2 COMMON MAMMAL TRACKS

with trotting or running. Notice that the nails of a cat, ordinarily retracted while traveling, do not leave an imprint as do those of the dog.

Snow offers several clues concerning how recently the animal has passed. Some melting occurs even on cold days. Fresh tracks are sharp and show clean, slick bottoms. Older tracks, especially those present for two or three days, become less distinct. During a continous fall, filled tracks are older.

## OTHER THINGS TO DO

Tracks left clearly in soil or mud can be faithfully and attractively reproduced in plaster. Clean out loose twigs, grass, and dirt. Pour in about a one-inch depth of plaster of Paris which has been mixed with water to the consistency of cake batter. The plaster will dry sufficiently in one hour, unless the ground is wet or the mix thin. With a knife, carefully cut the cast out of the soil. Clean and label it with the animal's name, your name, location, and date.

Seton mentions that photographed tracks make a fair showing, provided the light is angled enough to throw shadows. He likewise tells how to record on paper the prints of animals chased through spilled ink or black paint.

# Nerves and Brain

## 15
## FROG NERVES

**Materials.**
1. Frogs
2. Dissecting instruments
3. Ether and cotton

**Introducing the brain and nerves.** At the top of the human head, securely enveloped in the bony cranium, is a fifteen-billion-cell structure which we call the brain. This enormously complex jellylike mass is armed with an assortment of nerves with which it sees and knows the outside world. Each nerve is composed of thousands of individual nerve fibers called *neurons*. These units may be up to several feet in length but so thin as to be invisible to the unaided eye. Minute electrical impulses passing via neurons are what keep the brain and world united. Through these it is informed by the senses, and through these it transmits directions to the muscles and glands.

Scientists separate the nervous system into three divisions: (1) central, (2) peripheral, and (3) autonomic. Each system is closely interrelated with the others, but for convenience we shall study them separately.

**The central nervous system.** The *central* nervous system is composed of the *brain* and *spinal cord*. These integrate information and bring about some response. Simple responses, such as the jerking motion which follows a tap on the knee, are controlled entirely by the spinal cord. More complex reactions, such as the recognition of objects, words, and sounds, involve the brain entirely or in conjunction with the spinal cord.

**The peripheral nervous system.** *Peripheral* nerves are all those (except autonomics) which carry impulses toward and away from the brain and spinal cord. Those leading to the brain are called *sensory* nerves. They detect and convey impressions of light, sound, heat, cold, touch, pain, and other sensations. On the other hand, *motor* nerves carry impulses away from the central nervous system. They are named motor nerves because they produce movement due to contraction of muscles.

Grasp a hot object and what happens? You release it, of course, and yell "ouch" or some less polite word. Here is a perfect illustration of nerve reactions. Heat indirectly generates electrical impulses which journey to the spinal cord along sensory neurons. There they transfer almost at once to motor neurons leading back to muscles of the hand. The hot object is dropped. In the meantime, secondary central nerve fibers have discharged impulses to the brain where heat is recognized as a painful sensation. Now you yell. This involves motor nerves to the vocal cords and mouth. And it all happens in but a fraction of a second.

A curious matter, which confirms the nature of sensory nerve impulse transmission, is the existence of "phantom limbs." Amputation of a leg, for instance, is no guarantee that it will no longer seem present. Frequently pain in the missing foot is noticed, or the limb may be felt in some particular position. Such occurrences are believed due to irritants developing near the cut nerve. Electrical impulses caused by these are the same as before amputation and will be so interpreted.

**The autonomic nervous system.** *Autonomic* nerves regulate the heart, blood vessels, intestines, and most of the other internal glands and organs of the body. The neurons act involuntarily; one cannot readily change their actions by his own will (although a few yogis have become masters of the autonomics and slow their hearts when desired). This system consists of two different types of nerves: sympathetic and parasympathetic.

Think back to the most horrifying experience of your life. Perhaps it was a nightmare . . . and in it you are walking near a dark cemetery. From the bowels of the earth a skeleton hurtles toward you. Pale from fright, you find your hair standing on end. You start to run. Your heart beats rapidly as more and more blood rushes to moving muscles. Respiratory passageways enlarge to bring in more air. With pupils enlarged and heart still pounding, you awaken to discover it was nothing but a dream. *Sympathetic* nerves sped your heart, opened your pupils, and governed your general appearance. They perform similarly in any emergency, whether you are the aggressor (as in fighting) or the one running away.

*Parasympathetic* nerves are active during periods of rest. They tend to conserve energy needed for briefer emergencies. Upon stimulation of these nerves, the heart slows, air passages narrow, pupils contract, and the hair is at ease. Blood is diverted to the stomach and intestines where digestion speeds up. Note that most of the parasympathetic effects are just the reverse of sympathetic effects.

Autonomic nerves in the frog are small and not easily recognized. In the present dissection only the brain and spinal nerves will be considered.

## DISSECTING AND STIMULATING SPINAL NERVES

Put a frog in a closed container with ether-soaked cotton and leave it until it has expired. Remove the frog and place it on its back. Open the animal's chest and abdominal cavities and remove all internal organs. In the chest this includes the heart, lungs, and esophagus. In the abdomen take out the stomach, intestines, liver, spleen, kidneys, and all associated structures (Figs. 29–1 and 29–3). If possible, combine the dissections of Chapter 29 and this project to avoid waste of animals.

*Spinal nerves* (containing both motor and sensory neurons) pass from the spinal cord through openings in the vertebrae (bone segments) of the backbone. These nerves are always paired. In the frog there are ten pairs (Fig. 15–1). In mammals there are usually more (thirty-one pairs in man).

The second spinal nerves are very large, compared to the others. These are white, tough strands of tissue arising from the spinal cord in the chest region. Usually the second nerves are joined by branches from spinal nerves one and three. These pass into the arm as the *brachial* nerve. Pinch the two brachial nerves with forceps. Note contraction of muscles in the arm supplied by each nerve. This demonstrates the presence of motor fibers.

Attempt to locate spinal nerves four, five, and six. These are very small. Pinch each and observe contraction of muscles at the sides of the body.

Spinal nerves seven, eight, nine, and ten are easily seen. These pass through the backbone and extend directly toward the tail region. Nerves eight and nine are particularly large. The four paired nerves

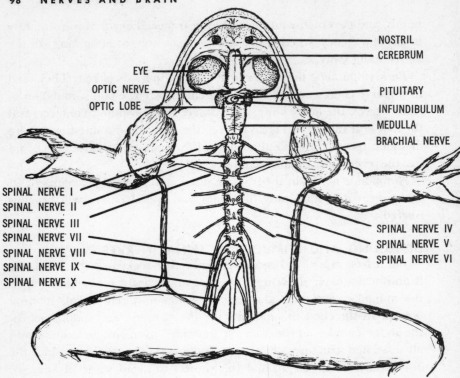

Fig. 15–1 VENTRAL VIEW OF THE FROG'S NERVOUS SYSTEM

on each side join in the leg to form the *sciatic nerve.* Pinch a sciatic and see the leg kick.

**Dissection of the brain.** With the frog still on its back, cut away the lower jaw and tongue to expose the roof of the mouth. Locate the first vertebra of the neck, the one nearest the head. Carefully insert the tip end of a scissors blade between this and the thin bony membrane of the mouth. Cut forward slowly, being careful not to push the scissor tips into the underlying medulla (Fig. 15–1). Remove bits of bone with forceps. Continue cutting and chipping away until the entire ventral (under) side of the brain is uncovered.

Identify each of the structures shown in Fig. 15–1. Between the eyes is the *cerebrum,* an organ for thinking, very large and more complex in man (Fig. 15–3). Behind the eyes are *optic lobes* from which optic nerves pass to the eyes. These structures, as you may have reasoned, are concerned with vision. Between optic lobes the *pituitary*

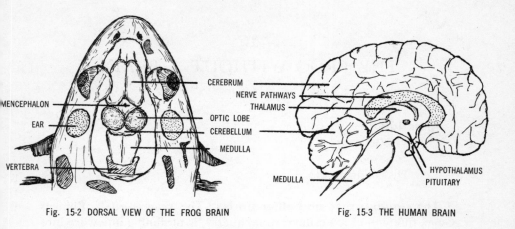

Fig. 15-2 DORSAL VIEW OF THE FROG BRAIN                    Fig. 15-3 THE HUMAN BRAIN

rests, surrounded by an *infundibulum*. At the rear of the head region is the *medulla,* an important heart and breathing-control center which governs the autonomic nervous system.

With heavy scissors, continue to cut away bone. Try to remove the intact brain from the skull. Locate the *thalamencephalon* on the dorsal (top) side between the cerebral hemispheres and the optic lobes (Fig. 15–2). This corresponds to the *thalamus* in man, an area which recognizes crude sensations such as pain or extremes of temperature. Find also the *cerebellum,* a small body between the optic lobes and medulla. The cerebellum aids an individual in maintaining balance and regulates movement.

## OTHER THINGS TO DO

Comparative studies of anatomy are always valuable and this is especially true for the nervous system. Continue your endeavors by dissecting the nerves and brains of fish, birds, and mammals. Notice the evolutionary trend toward greater volume and that various lobes of the brain vary in size, depending partly on the extent to which they are used. Preserved specimens from biological supply houses may be used for most of this work.

A popular account which will further introduce you to the central nervous system is J. Pfeiffer, *The Human Brain,* Harper and Brothers, New York, 1955.

# 16

# THE FROG WITHOUT A BRAIN

**Materials.**
1. Frog
2. Scissors
3. Dissecting needle

**The crowbar case and other stories.** The year is 1848. Phineas Gage, foreman of a Vermont stone quarry, is pushing gunpowder into the hole of a rock. Suddenly . . . an explosion. The crowbar now has passed into the left side of his face and protrudes from the top of his skull. Gage is stunned, but within an hour he walks with assistance to a doctor. Following surgical treatment, he recovers and returns to work but no longer as foreman. This curious accident removed the front areas of the brain, areas which inhibit civilized men but left Gage irresponsible, impatient, profane, and obstinate. Despite the change of personality, his skill and memory are little altered. Other areas of the brain take over these functions.

This true case history has been repeated over and over again in the past quarter century, but the surgeon's scalpel replaces the crowbar and hospitals replace the stone quarries. There is a reason for this, a very serious mental reason. The patients operated upon are psychotics—terrified, depressed, suicidal. Removal or separation of pathways to the front of the brain is a last resort, but effective in two thirds of the cases. Those so treated lose their fears and care less for what goes on about them. Some return to normal life after years of absence, but many are never quite the same. They lack restraint, similar to Phineas Gage, and never show real ambition or drive.

Since the early 1950s, human brain destruction has been falling into disfavor. A different approach, the use of tranquilizer drugs has been substituted. These act directly on the brain, affecting both central and autonomic nervous systems. They relax agitated minds of mental patients and make them more susceptible to psychiatric care.

**Goltz's dog.** Surgical study of human brains is limited, but man's inquisitiveness is not. To close intellectual gaps, brains of animals have been used extensively. In 1874, Friedrich Leopold Goltz, a German physiologist, was the first to remove the full cerebrum of a higher animal. He chose a dog which eventually achieved international fame, surpassing even that of Goltz himself. After surgery, this brainless creature was often restless, pacing the floor continuously. Its emotions were obviously impaired, for there was neither recognition of friends nor fear of enemies. Feeding and drinking were not voluntarily performed. Goltz's dog and other decerebrate animals require loving, motherly care to remain alive, but from these patient studies come operations to relieve human sufferings.

**Areas of the brain.** One need not remove the whole brain to get altered performances. Destruction of only part of the outer layer of gray matter, or *cortex* of the cerebrum may weaken or disorient movements of the hands or feet or cause disabilities in hearing, vision, smell, speech, or writing. It all depends on what part and how much of the brain is damaged.

Scientists have even more accurately pin-pointed the areas by stimulating with very weak electric currents the brains of lightly anesthetized animals. This is often done in a region called the *motor cortex,* which lies near the center of the cerebrum. If they stimulate the top, foot muscles contract. If they stimulate the bottom, face muscles contract. It is a curious thing that many of the brain's representations of the body are inverted in respect to the body's geometry; this holds for the *sensory cortex* as well, an area behind the motor cortex, which feels sensations of touch, heat, cold, and pain.

One very interesting point has arisen from these studies. The part of the body most used by an animal gets the biggest area on the cortex. For instance, monkeys, who swing in trees and feel objects with their lips, have correspondingly large areas for their hands and mouths. Pigs are almost all snout, as far as the brain goes, for this is what they root with.

**Electric waves from brains.** The brain is not a silent organ. It forever emits small but significant waves of electricity. To measure this activity, wires leading from a machine called the *electroencephalograph* are attached to the scalp. Rapid wavy lines of electricity thus recorded have intriguing experimental possibilities.

People with eyes open have a minimum of electrical activity, but when the eyes are closed, characteristic waves of eight to ten cycles per second generally appear. These do not show in visual thinkers, those who picture images in their minds even when their eyes are closed and "see" these in color. On the other hand, certain people have waves which are always present, whether their eyes are open or closed. These are abstract thinkers. They do not visualize. When persons of such extreme types meet, they often clash. Neither understands the other's mode of reasoning.

People who are intolerant and easily frustrated show slower than normal brain waves. It has been found that an identical wave rate could be produced in calm and tolerant types by slowly flickering lights in front of the eyes. What happens? You guessed it. Nice people get very aggravated as their brain activity decreases in rate due to the flicker.

More practically the electroencephalograph has been used to locate tumors and show tendencies for epileptic convulsions. Other studies hint at correlating certain rhythms with juvenile delinquency and crime. Dr. W. Grey Walter has expanded upon this in his book, *The Living Brain,* W. W. Norton and Company, Inc., New York, 1958.

## DESTROYING THE BRAIN AND SPINAL CORD OF A FROG

Observe the normal frog for a few minutes. Watch him swim and jump. Rub the animal's sides to get a croak. Watch him turn over when placed on his back.

Now you will study what happens when the brain is removed. Push one blade of heavy, sharp scissors across the back of this frog's mouth (Fig. 16–1). Make sure the edge hits both corners of the mouth. Cut

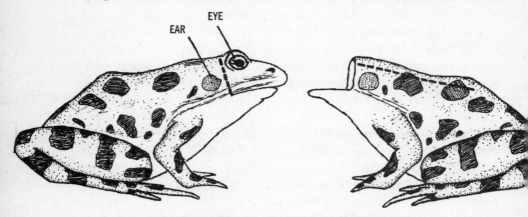

EYE

EAR

Fig. 16–1 DESTRUCTION OF THE FROG'S NERVOUS SYSTEM
(FOLLOW THE DOTTED LINES)

off the top of the head (eyes included) with one fast stroke. This immediately destroys the cerebrum. The animal now feels absolutely no pain, despite its somewhat unwholesome appearance.

In a few minutes the frog recovers and assumes his normal body position. Give him a push and he jumps, but not without the push or some other stimulus. Place him in water. He swims, but if left to himself near a whole ocean of water, he will sit till he dries into nothingness. Stroke the sides to see if a brainless frog croaks. Place him on his back. He flips over normally. Turning over as well as the other positive responses observed are reflexes, which will be studied in Chapter 17. Reflexes here involve only the spinal cord, not the cerebrum.

The *spinal cord* is a whitish-colored mass of nerve tissue running down the center of the back. Push a dissecting needle down the cord (Fig. 16–1). The animal jerks and finally stiffens out, due to stimulation of *motor nerves* (those which control movement). This is not painful since he no longer receives sensations at the previously destroyed brain. Upon withdrawal of the needle, the frog becomes completely limp. There is no longer a central nervous system to receive and dispatch nerve impulses. None of the previously obtained reflexes can now be elicited. Your frog, which has neither brain nor spinal cord, is said to be *double pithed*.

Several bodily structures will continue to function for a short time—those which are independent of nerve control. The heart is the most easily demonstrable of these. Open the chest cavity and see it still beating.

If you have time now, proceed to a later experiment (for instance, Chapter 26 on muscle contraction) requiring pithed animals. This will conserve frogs.

## OTHER THINGS TO DO

Animals vary in response, depending on their position in the evolutionary scale. Removing the "brain" of a worm has little effect (actually there are several brains, but they are only knots of nerve tissue). The remaining portion quickly crawls away and goes about its business. The frog is somewhat altered as seen here, but not greatly so until the spinal cord is also destroyed. However, removal of the cerebrums of birds or mammals alters their "personalities" in a very striking manner.

If you appreciate surgery, you may be interested in the operation described by D. E. Stulken and W. A. Hiestand, "The decerebrate pigeon," *Turtox News,* volume 27, December 1949. Do not attempt this more difficult procedure unless you have become skilled at surgery suggested in the endocrine section of this book. Decerebrate wild pigeons become tame and stuporous, sitting for hours with feathers erect and eyelids at half-mast. If placed on a hot pavement, they lift first one foot and then another, but never move off.

# 17

# REACTIONS AND REFLEXES

**Materials.**
1. Ruler or yardstick
2. Stop watch (or watch with second hand)
3. Cup or beaker with water
4. Stethoscope (which can be homemade)

**Reactions versus reflexes.** What happens when a doctor taps your knee? The leg jerks. Is conscious effort involved? No. This is an example of a *reflex,* an involuntary movement resulting from some stimulus. Not all reflexes are as simple as a knee jerk. Some require the co-ordination of many muscles. Standing and walking are examples. Even with these, no conscious effort is required.

*Reactions* are movements made consciously. The ball is pitched; you swing the bat. The light turns green; you cross the street. In each case the mind recognizes a situation and brings about some response.

**The time for reaction.** A child steps from behind a parked car near a grade school. An approaching motorist slams on the brakes . . . too late. It takes but a fraction of a second to react, but a fraction is sometimes too long. At thirty mph, more than twenty feet pass before a driver applies the brake. Many more feet are required for a complete stop. Modern aviators have even greater difficulties. If two rocket pilots approach head on at 1500 mph, each pilot will move about one quarter of a mile before he responds to the other's presence.

Simple visual and touch reactions require about 0.2 or 0.3 seconds, with much variation among individuals. Reactions to pain and hearing are quicker. Complex reactions are slower. A motorist making a stop, for example, must first observe and recognize, then move from accelerator to brake and push in. All this requires almost three quarters of one second.

**Reaction-time variations.** Reaction time varies with the intensity of a stimulus. Response to dim light may be two or three times slower than to bright light. This reflects an increased time for decision. On the other hand, loud noises and acute pain are very swiftly recognized. In daylight, objects directly in the line of sight are most rapidly perceived and reacted to. In the dim light of night, we see and respond best by looking to one side of that which we wish to recognize. Scientists have explained this paradox by showing that cells for bright vision are packed near the center of the eye, while distinctly different cells for faint vision are located at its periphery.

States of excitement and increased attention shorten the time for reaction. Inattention, worry, and fatigue prolong this time. In driving, one must remain always alert to road conditions. Deep thought or too much conversation will distract and delay reactions. Prolonged driving should not be undertaken without frequent stops.

**What the doctor learns from reflexes.** There are many different reflexes which can be tested. Each reflex shows the response of some particular muscle or groups of muscles. If there is no response or an exaggerated response, the physician suspects damage. Perhaps the nerves are at fault, perhaps the muscles. In any case the testing of reflexes gives some clue to the area of difficulty.

## HOW QUICK ARE YOUR EYES AND FINGERS?

It is difficult in most home or high-school laboratories exactly to measure time units in fractions of a second. However, the distance through which an object falls is not hard to measure, and from this it is easy to calculate the time involved.

To perform this test, one person holds a ruler by the twelve-inch mark (Fig. 17–1). A second person places his thumb and first finger near to, but not touching, the zero-inch mark. The first person releases the ruler, and the second grabs it as soon as he sees it fall. Note the distance of fall and compare with the following table to find reaction time.

Table 1   REACTION TIME OBTAINED FROM DISTANCE OF FALL

| Fall in inches | 4 | 5 | 6 | 7 | 8 | 9 | 10 |
|---|---|---|---|---|---|---|---|
| Time in seconds | 0.14 | 0.16 | 0.18 | 0.19 | 0.20 | 0.22 | 0.23 |

| Fall in inches | 11 | 12 | 13 | 14 | 15 | 16 | 17 |
|---|---|---|---|---|---|---|---|
| Time in seconds | 0.24 | 0.25 | 0.26 | 0.27 | 0.28 | 0.29 | 0.30 |

For more accurate calculations use the formula:

$$\text{time in seconds} = \sqrt{\frac{\text{fall in inches}}{192}}$$

Usually the ruler will fall eight or ten inches before it is caught, but if you divert the subject's attention, it will fall farther. Have him do some mental arithmetic. Drop the ruler and determine whether his reaction time is now prolonged. Use the average of several trials.

A variation of this experiment is to bet someone that he cannot catch a dollar bill if you drop it. Have him place his fingers over, but not touching, the picture of George Washington. Drop the bill. The loss of money by this means is extremely rare.

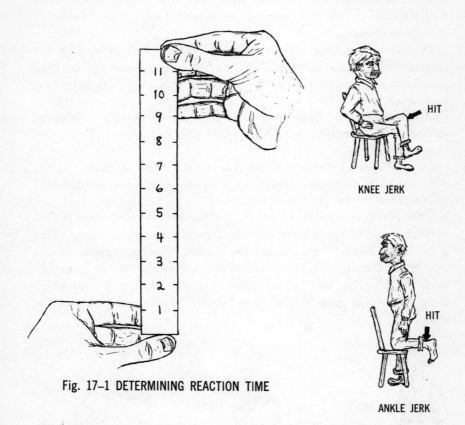

Fig. 17–1 DETERMINING REACTION TIME

KNEE JERK

ANKLE JERK

**Passing hand clasps.** This experiment requires the co-operation of the members of a group. All join hands and form a circle. The person at the head of the line squeezes the hand of the person on his right and at the same time starts a stop watch. The hand clasp is then passed as quickly as possible around the circle. When it again reaches the starting position, the stop watch is stopped. The total time is then divided by the number in the circle to get the average reaction time to hand pressure. Timing may be accomplished somewhat less accurately by using the second hand of an ordinary watch or clock.

**A few simple reflexes (Fig. 17–2).** *Knee jerk.* Using the side of the hand, strike just beneath the knee of another person sitting with crossed legs. The leg jerks. In this case the *patellar ligament* over the kneecap is stretched. Impulses are sent through the spinal cord, which causes contraction of muscles in the lower limb.

*Ankle jerk.* Stand beside a chair, but with one leg kneeling on the seat. Let a second person quickly strike the back of your ankle. Your foot jerks backward. This reflex involves stimulation of the *tendon of Achilles* in the ankle.

*Posture reflex.* In a normal standing posture the calf muscles are partially relaxed. Lean forward while a friend feels your calf muscles. Leaning causes reflex contraction of these muscles and thereby prevents a fall.

*Abdominal reflex.* Rapidly draw a finger across someone's abdomen just beneath the bottom ribs. Abdominal muscles contract. The abdomen draws in.

*Cardiac sphincter reflex.* There is a circular band of muscle at the entrance to the stomach which controls the admission of food and water. This is the *cardiac sphincter.* Place a stethoscope (or ear) against a friend's left abdominal wall. Have him swallow some water. Listen! In about six or eight seconds a gurgling sound is heard. This is caused by a reflex relaxation of the cardiac sphincter muscle. Water now enters the stomach. If no stethoscope is available, it can be simply made by plugging two rubber tubes into your ears and connecting them through a glass Y-tube to a funnel. The funnel picks up the sound.

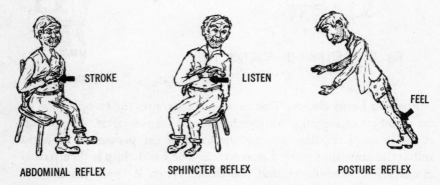

ABDOMINAL REFLEX            SPHINCTER REFLEX            POSTURE REFLEX

Fig. 17–2 LOCATIONS OF VARIOUS REFLEXES

## OTHER THINGS TO DO

Reactions and reflexes may be seen in many animals other than man. Remember the last time you scratched your dog's belly: he kicked, a reflex designed to remove itchy things. Similarly, if you put paper soaked in dilute acetic acid on a frog's back, he will forcefully remove it with his hind feet. This is an involuntary act. Animals with missing brains still respond to tickling sensations, but pithing the spinal cord halts this as well as other reflexes.

More exacting technical experiments have pin-pointed the nerves and sections of the spinal cord controlling each reflex function. In these the cord is severed after cutting through the backbone. It has been found that nerves in the neck control the arms and hands, those of the trunk regulate respiration, and those lower down move the feet. Usually such operations have very temporary effects, except in man and, to a lesser extent, apes. Operative techniques for spinal-cord sectioning are given by F. E. D'Amour and F. R. Blood, *Manual for Laboratory Work in Mammalian Physiology,* University of Chicago Press, Chicago, 1954.

# 18

# ANIMAL INTELLECT

**Materials.**
1. Puppy, kitten, and/or other animal
2. Meat or other food
3. Several feet of wire fence
4. Mirror
5. Watch with second hand

**How experience "conditions" behavior.** Have you noticed the excitement of a dog at mealtime? As soon as the refrigerator door rattles, his mouth waters and he leaps about in ecstasy. But when puppies first see a refrigerator, they make no such response. Only after it is associated with food do they learn to anticipate. The famed Russian physiologist, Ivan Pavlov, was first to utilize the learned, or *conditioned response* for the benefit of science. He experimented with dogs, determining in each case how much saliva they released when food was brought in their presence. Next he rang a bell shortly before they were fed. After sufficient trials, the animals answered the bell by salivating, even when food was withheld. However, if their meal was too often absent, bell ringing evoked no reply. Pavlov observed that other stimuli (lights, odors) could be associated with the same or other responses (movement, changes of respiration and heart rate).

The Russian's conditioning procedures enable scientists to find the exact limits of animal sensations. They analyzed responses to very high or low notes and discrimination of pitches close on the musical scale. They explored the boundaries of light, color, odor, touch, and other perceptive capacities.

**Learning a maze.** Probably you too have taken a pencil and drawn your way through the alternate pathways of a printed maze. The idea is to start at one point and get to another without crossing lines or running up blind alleys. Humans have little trouble with such problems, not because of superior intellect but because they use their eyes before they use their pencils. Psychologists employ mazes with raised sides and require subjects to feel their way through while blindfolded. This is more difficult.

Ants and even worms grope along mazes and with practice become increasingly accurate. Mice and rats are faster learners; in fact, rats sometimes make fewer mistakes than college students! Certain rats have been specially bred to outperform their fellows. Unfortunately, this "brilliance" does not overlap into other areas of intelligence.

Ordinary mazes have limits. They will not differentiate the mentalities of animals more highly evolved than rodents, and we humans honestly believe we are smarter than the others. Special mazes have been built which call for alternating right with left turns. Usually the animal makes two right turns during the first trial. Next time he makes two left turns for the same purpose, and later two right turns, and so forth. Rats fail to solve this problem after a thousand attempts. Raccoons learn a couple of correct responses, and monkeys extend the series to eight, but no further. Young human children do poorly, but adults have no difficulty.

**Additional measures of animal mentality.** A more advanced test of comprehension is obtained by using *delayed responses*. As an example, food is placed under a triangular, but not a circular, piece of wood. Hungry, observant animals immediately remove the triangle and start eating. If taken from the room, rats forget the food location. Monkeys remember for some time and humans almost indefinitely.

But the true mark of intellect is reason, or insight. A chimpanzee placed in a cage with two jointed sticks, neither of which is long enough to reach a banana outside, may poke around a bit and then, rather suddenly, fit the sticks together and draw in his prize. As we say, "he's seen the light." Monkeys and chimpanzees occasionally find solutions overlooked by their keepers. A psychologist once dangled a banana from the ceiling and put several boxes on the floor near his chimpanzee. The animal, disregarding all boxes, led the psychologist to a point under the banana and then scrambled up the man's body to reach the piece of fruit.

## HOW BRIGHT IS YOUR PET?

If you have a dog, cat, or other reasonably intelligent pet, give him a try at this simple test. Stretch a curved piece of wire fence, about six feet in length, directly in front of him. Drop some favorite morsel of food behind the fence. What is the reaction? A young puppy usually scratches and barks for some time before wandering to the other side. A chicken takes much longer. Older, more experienced dogs may go around at once, perhaps doubting your intelligence for trying such a trick. If your pet does not immediately solve the problem, try him two, three, or more times to see how quickly he becomes enlightened.

**How fast do you learn?** Pick out a short paragraph in this book. Hold a mirror in front of the page and commence reading the mirror image aloud as rapidly as possible. Note the duration of reading from start to finish. Now reread the same paragraph. It goes much faster, doesn't it? Repeat several times for maximum improvement.

In this test you become familiar with reversed print as well as the actual words of the paragraph. Reading aloud reinforces this acquaintance. Wait several days and again read the same passage. The time required will be much less than the original but greater than the final trial. As weeks and months pass, this recall diminishes, but never completely.

## OTHER THINGS TO DO

Animals are easily motivated to action when food is placed directly in front of their noses, as in the fence experiment. Conveniently for the scientist, dogs and human subjects respond simply to a pat on the head or a pat on the back. Rodents and most other animals need

Fig. 18–1 A SIMPLE RAT MAZE

stronger stimuli before they master complicated problems. If you want to try maze running, withdraw food or water from a rat one or two days before the test. When ready, put the appropriate reward at one end of a maze similar to the one shown in Fig. 18–1. Put the animal at the other end. Curiosity, prodded by hunger or thirst, will cause him to explore the various passageways till his goal is achieved. Allow the animal to eat or drink his fill; then remove him to his original cage. Repeat the test twice daily, feeding (or watering) your rat only during the tests. Record the time and number of incorrect turns during each of several runs. Eventually the rat will make no further errors.

If possible, read the stimulating introductory discussion of psychological testing and animal wisdom by V. Packard, *Animal I.Q.,* The Dial Press, New York, 1950. Another excellent book, thoroughly documented with experimental methods, is that written by J. P. Scott, *Animal Behavior,* University of Chicago Press, Chicago, 1958.

# Special Senses

## 19

## INTRODUCING THE SENSES

**Materials.**
1. Scissors
2. Ruler
3. Thermometer
4. Small beakers or cups
5. Small piece (about 4"×6") of cardboard and a pencil
6. Sugar, raw potato, green apple, beet, turnip, and/or other similar foods

**How we perceive.** The beauty of a starlit night, the comfort of a campfire's warmth, the pleasure of a caress—these are life's sensations. Man builds machines now which play an acceptable game of chess and which mathematically outperform the world's great thinkers. His devices observe and record but never do they react emotionally. The senses and the mind place man over matter.

When animals see or hear or feel, it is not through any difference in the type of impulses traveling within nerves. The type of sensation depends on (1) the type of *receptor* (sense organ) which has been stimulated, and (2) the part of the brain which picks up the information. For example, light comes only through the eye, not the ear. Changes in the photoreceptors of the eye produce impulses traveling through nerves to the back of the brain, where vision is interpreted. It has been recognized for some time that if one could cross the nerves for vision and sound (causing them to go to the wrong brain areas), one would "see thunder and hear lightning."

**Exceptional and ordinary senses.** There are male moths with a sense of smell so highly developed that they can locate a mate from seven miles distance. Bats fly in total darkness, through rooms loaded with obstacles, by emitting sounds (usually inaudible to the human ear) which bounce off objects and back to their sensitive ears. A similar method of navigation has been demonstrated in the cave-dwelling guacharo bird of South America. The pit viper snake and blood-sucking insects locate prey from the heat of the victim's body. These are but a few of the many unusual adaptations of sense organs in animals.

The more commonly recognized senses of most animals can be separated into four categories: (1) *distance,* (2) *contact,* (3) *visceral,* and (4) *proprioceptive.* Those concerned with reception from a distance are *sight, sound,* and *smell.* Those involving external contact are *taste, touch, temperature,* and *pain.* The visceral, or internal organ receptors recognize vague sensations of *temperature, pain,* and *sickness.* Proprioceptive senses are those concerned with *balance* and *position.* In this chapter we shall briefly study position, touch, temperature, taste, and smell.

## FINDING YOUR FINGER

Cut a circular hole one cm. (about one-third inch) in diameter from the center of a piece of cardboard. Hold this in your left hand with one finger placed at the hole. Hold a pencil in your right hand and move this toward the hole with eyes open. Can you hit your finger? Now do the same with eyes closed, repeating the test eight or ten times. This test demonstrates the importance of vision in locating position, but also shows that approximations can be made even without sight. Such approximations are determined through stretch and compression of proprioceptors in the muscles, tendons, and joints.

**Tests for touch.** Obtain scissors with sharp points at the cutting end. Have a friend shut his eyes. Place one or both of the points lightly against the surface of his (1) finger, (2) nose, (3) back of hand, and (4) back of neck. Determine the minimum distance between scissor points at which both can be distinctly felt. The fingers have many touch receptors. The points will be closest together here. The back of the neck is least sensitive. If two points on the neck are closer than one inch, they are often felt as one point.

Run fingers lightly through the hair of your arm. At the base of each hair is located a special touch receptor. Each hair acts as a lever. Upon bending, the touch sensation is magnified as it reaches the appropriate receptor. Cats' "whiskers" are especially sensitive in this respect because of their length.

**Cold hands, warm heart.** Heat water to 88, 92, and 96°F. Place the water in small beakers and apply these in various orders to another person's hand and chest. Record the actual temperature and have the subject tell which beakers feel warm and which feel cool in each location.

Trunk temperatures are several degrees warmer than those of the hands and feet. Objects which feel warm in the hand will usually feel cool when placed next to the chest or abdomen, and vice versa. Hands are better for estimating cool temperatures, and chests are more accurate for warm temperatures.

**Dry and wet tastes.** Wipe your tongue dry. Place a few crystals of sugar (or salt) on it. Is there any taste? Close your mouth and dissolve the crystals with saliva. Taste returns. The receptors for taste are located in miniature depressions of the tongue. Foods must be dampened in order to reach and penetrate these receptors.

**Smell aids taste.** Have another person shut his eyes and hold his nose. Put in his mouth a small piece of either raw potato, green apple, beet, or turnip. Have him chew once or twice, noting the absence or presence of any definite taste sensation, then identify the unknown substance. Repeat several times, using several of the foods. Smell plays an important role in the identification of food flavor. Little or no taste is present when odors are absent. Consistency of food is also important, and very often this alone will permit proper identification.

## OTHER THINGS TO DO

There is room for much research on sensory perception, especially in the areas of smell, taste, contact, and equilibrium. Because of less relative importance to man himself, biologists tend to neglect senses other than the eyes and ears. Reception in beasts is often different from reception in humans. Several of these unusual adaptations are described by N. J. Berrill, "Unseen world of taste and smell," *Science Digest*, 42:69, December 1957.

# 20

# THE EYES AND VISION

**Materials.**
1. Snellen or A.M.A. test chart
2. Flashlight, lamp, or other bright light
3. Paper

**Man's overworked eyes.** Our ancestors were nomads who roamed forests and plains in search of food. In nature they found a brilliant sun to light every move, moves which never demanded long attention to tasks at close range. Primitive eyes retained excellent vision throughout life.

Today we read, write, sew, manipulate machinery, and stay closed up in buildings. As a result, almost one third of high-school students and two thirds of draftsmen, stenographers, and garment workers have defective eyes. Compare this with the ten per cent of farmers and other outdoorsmen similarly afflicted. Man's vision has paid dearly for civilization.

Vision specialists now know that eyes work best in strong light, such as that in nature. They have demonstrated this by measuring muscle tension and eye blinks, among other things. In one such test, print was read by the light from ten-foot candles (common home lighting) and 100-foot candles (shade on a bright, sunny day) and compared. There was eleven per cent less muscular tension and twelve per cent less blinking with the brighter lighting. In another type of experiment, an industrial plant increased general illumination from two- to twenty-foot candles. Accidents dropped fifty per cent.

From such endeavors scientists assure us that:
1. *More light saves sight.* Students should use the most powerful fluorescent or diffused incandescent lamps which are commonly available.
2. *Contrast* makes work less fatiguing. White thread, not black thread, is most readily seen on a dark background.

3. *Large type* is best for reading. Some newspapers and magazines neglect this.
4. *Bright surroundings* are pleasant and easier on the eyes. Illuminate the entire room in addition to local light. Avoid dark rugs, desks, walls, and ceilings.
5. *Reduced glare* aids vision. Never face a bright lamp or other source of discomfort.

**What's in an eye?** Our globe-shaped eyes are buried in bone of the skull, well protected by this and the eyelids. If dust enters, fluid pours from tear glands to wash it out. It cannot get behind an eyeball because each is covered lid to lid by a thin, transparent tissue—the *conjunctiva.* Oil glands keep tears from overflowing, if there aren't too many. When stopped up, these glands form styes.

The eyeball has three coatlike layers (Fig. 20–1). The outer layer, the *sclera,* continues across the front as the "white" of the eye and then as the *iris,* or colored portion. In the middle is a *choroid coat,* black and well supplied with blood vessels. Innermost and of most importance is the *retina,* a layer containing nerve cells for light reception. A *lens,*

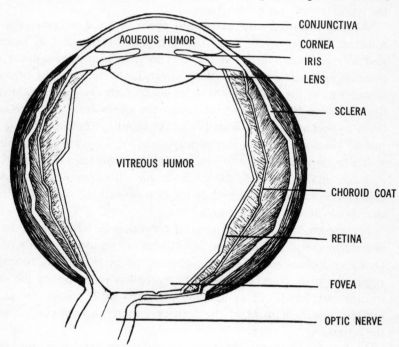

Fig. 20–1 THE ANATOMY OF THE EYE

lying just behind the *pupil's* circular opening, focuses light on these nerve cells. Without lenses, eyes are like cameras missing the same parts—the images taken are blurred. Finally, there are jellylike fluids which fill the eyeball and immerse its parts. These are the *aqueous humor* in front of the lens and the *vitreous humor* behind.

Each eye moves by means of six *muscles* attached to the outer coat. These cause the eyes to rotate in unison as an object is followed. If the muscles do not work in accord or if one is stronger than the others, "cross-eyes" may result.

**How do we see?** Light comes to your eye from a page in this book. The rays are bent and focused on the retina by the cornea and the lens, but the image is upside down. It is transmitted to the brain by the *optic nerve,* leading from the retina, where it is deciphered as being right side up.

"Upside-down" glasses have been made with special prisms to cause the image on the retina to be right side up. At first the brain interprets everything as inverted, but in several days it relearns and the world is again straight. If these glasses are taken off after the relearning period, the world is topsy-turvy once more.

**Accommodation and abnormal eyes.** Normal relaxed eyes see a distant tree very well. The lenses are pulled rather flat by ligaments and images focus clearly. If the eyes then look at a newspaper, they must *accommodate* to see the near object. Light rays must be bent more in order to be focused. Tiny muscles inside each eye contract, releasing the tension on the lens ligaments. Since the lenses are elastic, this causes them to become more rounded or curved and bends the entering rays, just as they are bent by a magnifying glass. Pupils dilate in distant vision to allow more light to enter. While reading, they constrict to give a clearer image. In old people the lenses have lost their elasticity and the eyes can no longer accommodate for near objects. So older people hold their books at arm's length to read.

*Hyperopia,* or farsightedness is a condition in which an individual sees distant objects clearly but has trouble accommodating for reading books or looking at other near objects. Light rays focus behind the retina for near objects because the eyeball is too short or the lens is insufficiently elastic. This may be corrected by a *convex,* or curved-out lens which helps bend the light rays more and converge them on the retina.

In *myopia,* or nearsightedness a person can read well, but cannot distinguish far objects. This may be caused by a long eyeball or a very elastic lens which causes light rays to focus in front of the retina. A *concave,* or curved-in lens is used to diverge the light rays and cause them to meet on the retina.

*Astigmatism* is a condition of blurred vision. This may be caused by unequal curvature of the cornea or lens and is corrected by a specially ground lens.

**Light and color.** Two types of *receptor* cells are in the retina. These are the *rods* and *cones*. The rods are for dim and twilight vision. Vitamin A deficiencies cause night blindness since the vitamin is used by the rods to make a visual substance. Cones function in bright light, transmitting the sensation of color to the brain. They are most highly concentrated in a tiny spot at the rear of the retina called the *fovea*. When you look directly at a single word on this page, it focuses on the fovea. All other words are dimmed, and those farthest away cannot be read at all.

Color blindness is an inherited tendency in which one has trouble distinguishing red from green. Color-blind people have trouble at stop lights. Among other more rare types of blindness there is one with complete absence of color vision. Such people see only black, white, and shades of gray. A number of animals have this problem, including dogs, cats, rats, and, believe it or not, bulls! In all these cases there is a deficiency of cone cells in proportion to rods.

## EYE TESTS

Examine a person with normal vision, using the Snellen or A.M.A. test chart. If possible, examine others with hyperopia and myopia without their glasses. Compare the results. A person with normal sight should be able to read the letters marked twenty feet at twenty feet. His vision is said to be 20/20. A person who can read only the letters marked thirty or forty feet at twenty feet has 20/30 or 20/40 vision.

Close first one eye and then the other while looking at Fig. 20–2. Are all the lines clear, or are some of them fuzzy? To a person who has astigmatism, the lines in one or more planes will be blurred and not so dark as others.

**Accommodation and pupillary reflexes.** Have a person stand in front of a window and look out. Then have him look at a speck on the window about one foot from his nose. Watch the pupil constrict. If he again looks out the window, the pupil will dilate.

Cover both eyes of the subject for a short while. Uncover them. See the pupils constrict from the increased amount of light.

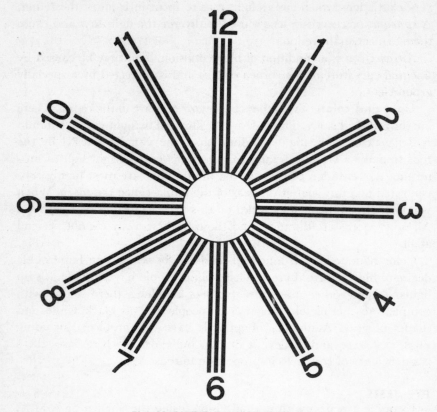

Fig. 20–2 TEST FOR ASTIGMATISM
Courtesy of American Optical Company

Shine a bright light into one eye and watch both pupils constrict. The constriction and dilation of the pupil are brought about by muscles in the iris.

**Which is your dominant eye?** Roll a piece of paper into a tube one or two inches in diameter. Using both hands, hold it about six inches in front of your eyes and look through it at an object across the room. Holding your hands steady, close first one eye and then the other. The eye which sees the object through the tube is your dominant eye.

**Hole in the hand.** Use the same roll of paper. Keep both eyes open. Hold the paper tube in front of one eye. Place your free hand a few inches in front of the other with palm toward you. Does this hand appear to have a hole in it?

**Blind spot.** Using the cross and face diagram (Fig. 20–3), close your right eye and look at the cross with your left eye. At about twelve to fifteen inches from your eye the face will disappear. Move the page back and forth to find the exact distance. Repeat with the left eye closed while looking at the face with your right eye. At the point where the optic nerve leaves the eye, there are no rod or cone light receptors. In this experiment we have shown that there is no vision at this point, appropriately named the *blind spot*.

Fig. 20–3 TEST FOR BLIND SPOT

**Afterimage.** Look at a bright light for several seconds, then glance away. You still see an afterimage, and these can sometimes be very colorful. Using the outline of an American flag, make one black star on a yellow background. Make the stripes alternating green and black. Gaze intently at this atrocious-looking flag for sixty seconds, then look at a white background. A red, white, and blue flag appears in all its old glory!

## OTHER THINGS TO DO
These experiments demonstrate several properties of the eye itself. Other simple tests, especially concerning the physics of light, will be found in UNESCO's *700 Science Experiments for Everyone,* Doubleday & Company, Inc., Garden City, New York, 1958.

An excellent project for those interested in anatomy is the dissection of sheep, cow, ox, or whale eyes (the latter are available from the General Biological Supply House). Consult Fig. 20–1 to locate the anatomical parts while doing your dissection. Comparison of mammalian with multifaceted insect eyes makes this study even more instructive. Each facet is an eye in itself, microscopically visible in one's own preparations but seen with more detail in supply-house slides. An article which deals with curiosities in the vision of beasts is J. G. Cook's "How animals see," *Science Digest,* 42:62, November 1957.

# 21

# THE EARS AND HEARING

**Materials.**
1. Watch or clock
2. Tuning fork

**Our carefully constructed ears.** Beyond the two obtrusive flaps popularly called ears are structures as intricate as those in fine Swiss watches—vibrating membranes, tiny bones, microscopic hair cells, and auditory nerves. These are the parts with which we hear—through darkness, around corners, outside the limits of our other senses. They are well protected by the hardest bones of the body, within which they lie.

The ear of which biologists speak is divided into outer, middle, and inner portions. The *outer ear* is the flaplike part, or *pinna* which channels sound through the *auditory canal* to the *eardrum* (Fig. 21–1). Dogs move their pinnae to locate and concentrate sound waves, but man has lost this ability, except perhaps for those few who can wiggle their ears. Wax in the auditory canal collects dust and repels bugs by its slight odor. It also causes a noticeable hearing deficiency for those who wash their ears infrequently. The eardrum is a thin muscular membrane which vibrates when hit by sound waves. Man's hearing is so acute that a movement of this membrane equal to one tenth the diameter of a hydrogen atom will be definitely perceived as sound.

In the *middle ear* there are three little bones, the *malleus, incus,* and *stapes,* or, as they are popularly called, hammer, anvil, and stirrup. The bones are set vibrating by the eardrum, to which the malleus is attached. From the middle ear leading to the back of the throat is a small opening called the *Eustachian tube.* In coming down mountains you may have experienced fullness in the head when this tube is closed. Suddenly there is a "pop" as it opens to equalize pressure between the ear and throat.

The stapes bone presses on a distensible membrane at the entrance to the *inner ear*. This membrane, called the *oval window,* is much smaller than the eardrum and moves through a greater distance. From here, mechanically reinforced oscillations penetrate the liquid-filled, snail-shaped *cochlea,* which contains cells having hairlike appendages. The hairs vibrate and generate electric impulses in the *auditory nerve* to which they are attached. As impulses arrive at the brain they are interpreted as sound, and all this in but a fraction of a second after the original waves reached the outer ear.

**Faithful reproduction of sound.** Experimenters in 1930 discovered that animal ears could serve as telephone receivers in a living communications system. To do this they anesthetized a cat and connected its auditory nerves with a loud-speaker in a soundproof room. As one scientist spoke into an ear, the other listened at the speaker. Exact reproductions of sound were obtained, even with a whisper! Here was an important tool for ear studies. Other researchers applied electrodes directly to the *basilar membrane* of the cochlea, upon which are found the hair cells. Sound was picked up, but only high notes were heard at the cochlea's base and low notes at its apex. Degenerate hair cells gave no response. It was concluded that vibration of the basilar membrane causes hair cells to generate electrical potentials, recognized by the brain (or a loud-speaker) as sound. Similar deductions were derived from other animals, including human cadavers in whom the response lasts for several hours after death.

In later experiments the reverse procedure was attempted—electric potentials were used to generate cochlear vibrations. Alternating currents passed through the ear caused a pitch directly proportional to current frequency. Even a speakerless radio connected to the head produced distorted but intelligible words and music.

## WHERE IS THE CLICK?

Click two coins together or snap your fingers in various positions about the head of a blindfolded subject. Ask him to point to the sound. He will guess correctly when the clicking is directly to the left or right, but he fails as the sound comes near the mid-line—in front, above, or behind.

We localize sound subconsciously by noting on which side it is louder (the head acts as a "shade") and at which side it first arrives. When noise is heard midway between the ears, the intensities and distances are equal at both ears. In this case, accurate location is purely a matter of chance.

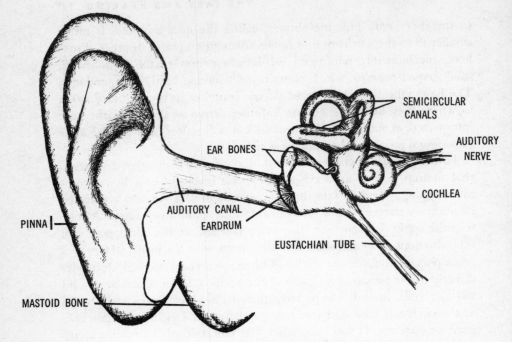

SEMICIRCULAR CANALS

AUDITORY NERVE

EAR BONES

COCHLEA

PINNA

AUDITORY CANAL
EARDRUM

EUSTACHIAN TUBE

MASTOID BONE

Fig. 21-1 PARTS OF THE EAR

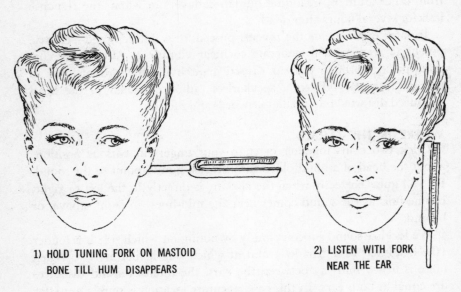

1) HOLD TUNING FORK ON MASTOID
BONE TILL HUM DISAPPEARS

2) LISTEN WITH FORK
NEAR THE EAR

Fig. 21-2 TEST FOR DEAFNESS

**Tests for deafness.** Gradually move a ticking watch away from the ear of a friend and record the distance at which it was last heard. Do the same for his other ear; then have him test you. Is hearing equally acute in left and right ears? Do you hear as well as your friend? Probably there will be some variations.

There are three classifications of partial or total deafness: (1) transmission, (2) perceptive, and (3) central. *Transmission deafness* is a natural accompaniment of aging. Often it results from the growing together of bones in the middle ear. This prevents conduction of sound pulsations. Hearing aids, which transmit sound through bone of the skull, help this condition immensely. Surgery works, too. A little opening, hardly larger than a pinhead, is cut through bone of the inner ear and covered with a flap of skin. Sound waves vibrate upon this and fluids inside to set up impulses from hair cells through the auditory nerve. Perceptive and central hearing losses are less frequent. *Perceptive deafness* is caused by injury to auditory nerve fibers. *Central deafness* derives from damaged hearing centers in the brain. Neither condition can be repaired nor helped by present-day hearing aids.

Physicians sometimes use the following test to find specific types of hearing loss. You might try the same. Vibrate a tuning fork and hold its handle on the mastoid bone, right behind the ear (Figs. 21–1 and 21–2). Listen until the hum has just disappeared; then hold the forked portion close to your ear. Do you still hear the hum (most people do) or is all quiet? Individuals with transmission deafness hear nothing once the tuning fork has been removed from the bone. Those having perceptive or central deafness hear little or no sound through either air or bone.

## OTHER THINGS TO DO

Research laboratories and hearing clinics are often equipped with *audiometers,* devices in which both intensity and pitch may be varied at will. Tests of hearing are conducted over the entire scale to find the exact extent of hearing loss. The range of high and low notes heard, particularly the low notes, is increasingly reduced as one grows older. Read about this and other experimental advances in the article by G. von Békésy, "The Ear," *Scientific American,* 197:66, August 1957.

# 22

# HOW ANIMALS BALANCE

**Materials.**
1. Frog
2. Large beaker or pan

**Gravity-free space.** With throttle wide open, the pilot pulls out of a dive and into an arclike trajectory. A pencil floats from its perch; the pilot hangs loose in his straps. There is no gravity for perhaps half a minute, and this is just the beginning. In space there will be no gravity for days, or even years, unless artificially supplied.

Is this dangerous? We cannot say for certain until man spends more time in the new gravity-free environment. At present it appears that men and animals can take it in stride as long as they keep their eyes open. With closed eyes, experiments have shown many mistakes in balance and position judgments.

**Sensations of balance.** There are three parts of the body which are primarily concerned with equilibrium: the *inner ears,* the *muscles,* and the *eyes.* Any change in position is ordinarily recognized by senses in all three of these parts.

It is the nature of animals to stay right side up and in their normal position. Attempts at change are immediately noted and met with resistance. As examples, animals will not remain on their backs when turned over, and they always land right side up when dropped. Exceptions are noted when the muscles, eyes, and inner ears are damaged or otherwise inactivated. All but the eyes become useless in a gravity-free environment.

**Earless turtles and gravity.** Many will recall tales about pioneer mice sent up in V-2s, Laika, the dog sent aloft in Russia's second Sputnik, and their many successors. Not very many will have heard the story of the first weightless turtle.

The turtle in question lost his inner ear balance mechanism when a terrarium was accidentally overheated. Thereafter, he was unable to strike at food and would sometimes swim upside down. Practice overcomes handicaps, and such was true in this case. In a few weeks the animal could once again balance and hit his food, but when scientists covered his eyes with a hood, he lost these abilities.

And now comes the climax. In a jet plane this turtle and several comrades were subjected to zero gravity. The injured animal could strike his food equally as well, with or without gravity. Normal turtles were completely disoriented without gravity, which is necessary for normal inner ear function.

From this experiment we conclude that training enables animals to do without their inner ears. The eyes become the chief organ of balance in this case. This has also been proved among flyers who, with practice, can learn to orient themselves visually despite a lack of gravity.

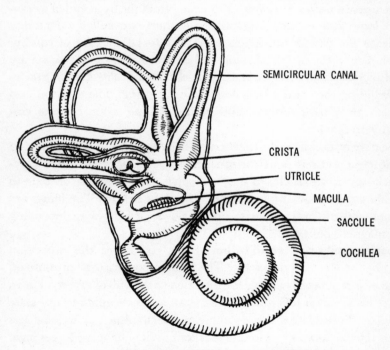

SEMICIRCULAR CANAL

CRISTA

UTRICLE

MACULA

SACCULE

COCHLEA

Fig. 22–1 THE LABYRINTH OF THE INNER EAR

**The labyrinth and equilibrium.** Within the inner ear is a maze of twisting, winding passageways called the *labyrinth* (Fig. 22–1). The labyrinth includes (1) a hearing apparatus and (2) structures concerned with balance—the *utricle* and *semicircular canals*. It also includes the saccule, an organ of uncertain importance, despite its similarity in structure to the utricle.

The utricle is alerted when the position of the body changes, as from lying to standing to standing on the head. It also reports car and elevator accelerations. In the utricle tiny rocklike particles are suspended from the ends of hairs in an organ called the *macula*. Gravity changes cause the particles to bend the hairs and thereby send out nerve impulses. The impulses, arriving at the brain, disclose position or the direction of an acceleration.

Semicircular canals are concerned with circular motions. When an individual turns, fluid moves through the canals, bending small hairs in the *crista,* an organ similar to the macula. The bent hairs send out nerve impulses which provide information about the direction of turn.

**The upside-down crayfish.** Projecting from the front end of a crayfish are long "feelers" called *antennae* and short ones called *antennules*. Cavities at the base of the feelers contain *statocysts,* organs of equilibrium similar to the utricle of man. Grains of sand in the statocysts are moved by gravity to produce sensations of balance. The external skeleton, including the statocysts, is lost during molting. The skeleton and statocysts grow back quickly, and grains of sand again become embedded in the cavities.

Researchers occasionally trick crayfish by sprinkling iron filings in their aquaria and removing the sand. At the time of molting, the crayfish pick up these particles in their statocysts. The animals continue to crawl about normally until a magnet is brought nearby. The filings are attracted and the crayfish swim upside down or sideways, depending on the magnet's position.

**Muscle senses and equilibrium.** Have you heard the expression "flying by the seat of your pants"? The feelings conveyed by pressure on the seat or feet generally denote the direction of the pull of gravity. For us who are earthbound this muscle sense is an accurate guide to our state of balance. For aviators this equilibrium mechanism has become less and less reliable as accelerations and other gravity changing forces have increased with speed.

Test your own muscle sense by leaning forward as far as possible. Do you fall? Of course not. Pressure due to stretching and compression of leg muscles alert the body to an impending fall. Automatic muscle reflexes prevent a topple even when the eyes are closed. Similar sensations are obtained in many different muscles and tendons (tendons are tough connective tissue attaching muscle to bone).

**The eyes and equilibrium.** In swimming there is no solid support for the muscles; hence, muscle sensations become negligible as balance indicators. If the eyes are shut, a person has left only the labyrinth of the inner ear to guide him. Swim underwater with eyes open, and it is quite simple to follow a straight line. Try the same feat with eyes shut and you will probably experience some difficulty in holding to your course, or even in holding to the same depth of water.

Many lesser animals can do very well without vision. Man, however, depends greatly upon his eyes. They have become his chief organs for maintaining balance.

## EQUILIBRIUM IN THE FROG

Place a frog in the center of a large beaker or pan. Rotate him and watch his head (and sometimes the entire body) move in a direction opposite to that of rotation. This is done in an effort to regain normal equilibrium. It is caused by a backward fluid flow within the semicircular canals (Fig. 22–2).

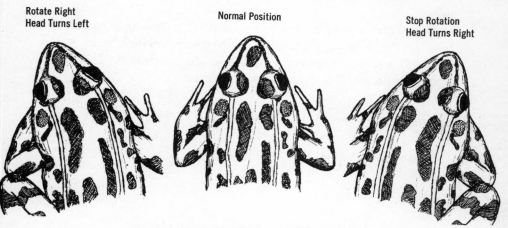

Fig. 22–2 ROTATION REACTIONS OF A FROG

Spin the animal rapidly (on a turntable if possible). After a while the fluid in the canals will catch up and move at the same speed as the animal himself. At this time hairs in the canals are no longer bent and the frog tends to turn his head back to a normal position.

Stop the rotation suddenly. The fluid, which was moving as fast as the frog, continues to flow. Which way does the frog lean? If the rotation was to the right, the fluid will flow to the right when he stops. The frog's brain responds to bending hairs in the canal and dictates that he also turn right.

Tilt the frog-containing beaker forward and backward. Observe compensatory equilibrium movements.

Turn the frog over on his back. He immediately flops over to his normal position. This is called the *righting reflex*.

**Rotating humans.** Humans and frogs react to gravity in much the same way, and our semicircular canals show only slight anatomical differences. Prove this to yourself by standing and turning quickly round and round eight or ten times. Stop now! Which way do you lean? Like the frog, you are clued in by the flow of canal fluids, and, like the frog, if you started by turning to the right you will now be falling to the right.

## OTHER THINGS TO DO

Shut your eyes after several body revolutions and quickly raise your index finger perpendicular to the ground. Have a friend watch. The task is not so easy as it sounds. The finger goes to one side just as the body does.

Almost any walking animal will substitute for the frog in equilibrium tests. Turtles are superb, since they can be rotated on their backs. Watch for slight jerking movements of the eyes after each trial. This also is frequently present in spinning human subjects.

# Endocrine Glands and Surgery

## 23
## TADPOLES, FROGS, AND THYROIDS

**Materials.**
1. Tadpoles
2. Thyroid powder and/or tincture of iodine
3. Thiouracil

**Clinician's view of the thyroid.** In the neck, slung across the windpipe like saddlebags on a bicycle, is a bilobed gland, an endocrine gland called the *thyroid* (Fig. 23–1). Like other members of the *endocrine* family, it secretes *hormones,* chemical travelers in the blood which orient diverse functions of the body. The thyroid's chief hormone is thyroxin, a product whose absence would make us humans a race of idiots and our beasts scrawny and unproductive.

Clinicians occasionally come face to face with total or near-total thyroid deficiency, a condition called *cretinism* if it appears in infancy. The unfortunate victims have potbellies, open mouths, protruding tongues, and inferior mentalities. In past centuries they sometimes grew to maturity, probably the source of stories about gnomes and other little people. Today a simple, thorough, almost miraculous cure awaits those treated early. The cretin need merely take thyroid pills or thyroxin derived from glands of domestic animals, but he must take these throughout life.

When adult thyroids degenerate, there is less change of intelligence, but physical appearance alters (skin is bloated) and there is increased susceptibility to cold and fatigue. Like chilled cars of ancient vintage, these people are slow starters and poor runners. To keep their engines warm they must wear heavy coats—sometimes in midsummer. In explaining these symptoms, we turn to the thyroid and find its chief characteristic is the maintenance of body temperature. It acts as a thermostat, switching on and off to regulate heat, activity, and oxygen consumption. If the hormone is scarce, the setting is low; if in excess, the setting is high, and the victims burn their candles at both ends.

The hormone thyroxin contains sixty-five per cent iodine in molecular combination. In regions where vegetables are grown in iodine-deficient soil, thyroids have difficulty in extracting enough of this important mineral. They enlarge, forming goiters, the bulges of which constituted a serious cosmetic problem prior to the early twentieth century. With the use of iodized salt, this annoyance has virtually disappeared.

**The endocrine family.** Step up beside a tall man, a basketball center, and you feel dwarfed. Now imagine looking up at a real giant, a man eight or nine feet tall. Such rare individuals actually exist, the result of an overactive *pituitary*. This tiny gland, located just beneath the brain (Fig. 23–1), secretes many hormones in addition to the one controlling growth. Some of these govern other endocrine glands: the thyroid, adrenals, and reproductive structures. Others control urination, the birth of young, and skin color of fish and amphibians.

Behind the stomach, a gland called the *pancreas* secretes digestive enzymes and *insulin,* the sugar-regulating hormone. Over two million people in the United States are afflicted with the insulin-deficient defect called *diabetes*. When this disease goes unchecked, sugar and acid increase in the blood, breathing is abnormal, coma appears, and finally death. Prior to 1922 there was no remedy. In that year a young surgeon, Frederick G. Banting, and his student, C. H. Best found methods for destroying pancreatic enzymes which digested insulin. They injected their hormone, extracted from the pancreas of dogs, into human patients, who obtained almost immediate relief. Daily use of insulin is still the preferred treatment, except for milder cases responding to sulfonamides or diet alterations. Sulfonamides are more convenient, however, since they may be taken by mouth.

Old-time surgeons recognized the problem of overactive thyroids and solved this by cutting them out. This cured the original ailment but created another which was sometimes fatal. In operating, they inadvertently destroyed the *parathyroids,* four little glands located within and behind the thyroid. These structures have a hormone which regulates body calcium and, indirectly, nerve and circulatory functions essential for life.

In anger, fear, or combat the heart beats faster, blood pressure rises, breathing tubes enlarge, and sugar is hastily freed from liver stores.

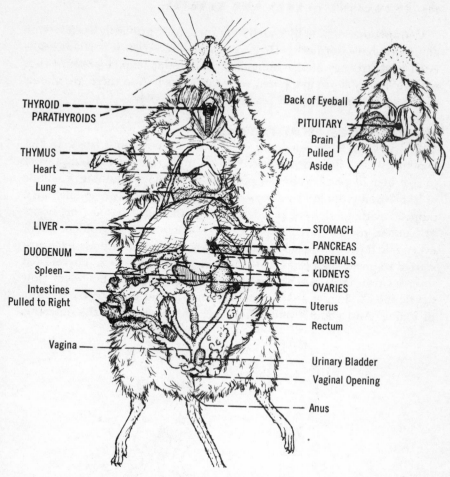

THYROID
PARATHYROIDS

Back of Eyeball

PITUITARY

Brain
Pulled
Aside

THYMUS
Heart
Lung

LIVER
DUODENUM
Spleen
Intestines
Pulled to Right

Vagina

STOMACH
PANCREAS
ADRENALS
KIDNEYS
OVARIES

Uterus

Rectum

Urinary Bladder
Vaginal Opening

Anus

Fig. 23–1 LOCATION OF ENDOCRINE GLANDS IN A MOUSE

Reactions of this nature are brought about by the hormone *epinephrine,*
released from sympathetic nerves and *adrenal glands.* They enable the
body to react quickly and energetically in time of need. Vital *cortical
hormones* (cortisone, hydrocortisone, and about thirty others) also come
from the adrenals. These have become invaluable remedies for arthritis
and similar painful inflammatory diseases.

Body contour, hair growth, sound of voice, and reproductive capacity
are controlled by hormones of the male *testes* and female *ovaries.* Removal of these glands yields a non-reproductive individual of neutral
sex. At one time this was a common practice for securing high-voiced
choir boys and trustworthy harem guards.

Certain other organs, although not functioning primarily as endocrine glands, do have hormones. Digestive enzyme secretion is partially regulated by hormones of the stomach and intestine. Blood pressure rises when a kidney hormone, *renin,* is overproduced. Also there are glands of uncertain importance, the pineal and thymus.

## MAKING FROGS FROM TADPOLES

Perhaps you have wondered what turns tadpoles into frogs. In this experiment you find the answer. Add 50 milligrams of thyroid powder to one liter of pond water (a pinch in a quart) containing a couple of large-sized tadpoles. In a second liter of water keep two equally large tadpoles without thyroid powder. Feed with boiled lettuce, or, better yet, put in moss-covered rocks. Change water (and thyroid powder) every few days. If you select tadpoles whose hind-limb buds have just started to grow, the results will be apparent in a few days. Thyroid-fed tadpoles transform quickly into frogs. Other tadpoles show very slow development (Fig. 23–2). If you have no thyroid powder, try tincture of iodine. Add about twenty drops per liter and watch the outcome.

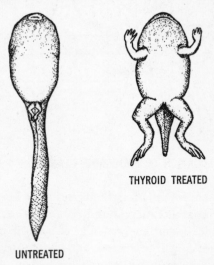

THYROID TREATED

UNTREATED

Fig. 23–2 THYROID EFFECT ON TADPOLES

*Metamorphosis,* or transformation has been prevented by experimentalists who completely remove tadpole thyroids. The animals grow to a very large size but never become frogs. *Thiouracil,* a drug which blocks iodine incorporation in thyroxin, has much the same effect.

Sprinkle 200 milligrams of thiouracil per liter in tadpole-filled water. Continue adding more each time you change water. The drug definitely delays and may even prevent metamorphosis.

## OTHER THINGS TO DO

Researchers applying thyroid to tadpoles have sometimes obtained frogs no larger than flies. If you are interested in small oddities, procure young tadpoles and start them on a lower, less toxic dose of the powder (5 to 10 mg./liter). Try bullfrogs for variety, as normally these remain tadpoles for two or three seasons.

Even more unusual metamorphoses have been produced in Mexican and western United States axolotls. Ordinarily these are aquatic salamanders complete with gills and broad swimming tails. When thyroid is placed in their water, they convert to land dwellers, a form never seen in nature!

Other aspects of thyroid function are worth investigating, such as its effect on oxygen uptake of rats (Chapter 28). If the thyroids are missing, oxygen uptake will decrease as it does during deficiency diseases. Surgical removal is performed by an incision in the neck, using operative techniques similar to those in Chapter 24. The entire procedure for rat thyroidectomy is given in F. E. D'Amour and F. R. Blood, *Manual for Laboratory Work in Mammalian Physiology,* University of Chicago Press, Chicago, 1954.

If you want a well-written beginner's book in endocrinology, obtain S. R. Riedman, *Our Hormones and How They Work,* Abelard-Schuman, Ltd., New York, 1956.

# 24

# THE REPRODUCTIVE SYSTEM

**Materials.**
1. Male mice (two or more)
2. Surgical instruments (sharp scissors and narrow forceps)
3. Ethyl or isopropyl (rubbing) alcohol
4. Cotton
5. Ether
6. Beakers
7. Heavy paper for anesthetizer
8. Surgical sewing needles and No. 50 thread

**Reproducing farm animals.** Champion beef or dairy bulls are animals well worth seeing and well worth the money spent on them—sometimes over $50,000 per bull. Beef cattle are bred to weigh more, in the right places, at smaller feed costs per pound. Dairy bulls sire cows which produce more and better milk. Increasing the reproductive potential of these first-class animals has long been the goal of agricultural scientists; and they have succeeded. Sperm, nowadays, can be artificially collected, diluted, refrigerated, and shipped throughout the world. When introduced into cows, these sperm fertilize eggs and produce calves having many desirable qualities of their father. In this way, a single bull may service hundreds or even thousands of cows.

The reproductive cells of roosters, stallions, and boars are not as readily stored as those of bulls. However, new techniques hold great promise. In the future, artificial fertilization may become feasible for many farm animals.

**The male reproductive tract.** Sperm-producing reproductive organs of males are called *testes* (singular, *testis*). Two of these hang in a sac called the *scrotum* (Fig. 24–1). Sperm is sensitive to temperature extremes. Special muscles draw the testes up (to a limited extent) on cool days and lower them as it gets warmer. Fertility of certain animals, such as rams, diminishes in hot weather unless they are sheared. Even man has not completely escaped this problem. Temporary sterility occasionally develops from high fevers.

Mature sperm is stored in the *epididymis,* adjacent to the testes, until mating occurs. During *ejaculation,* at the peak of sexual excitement, sperm is propelled up the *vas deferens* into the *urethra,* there to be joined

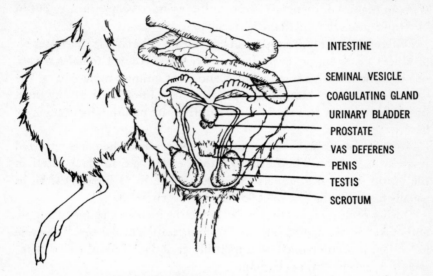

INTESTINE

SEMINAL VESICLE

COAGULATING GLAND

URINARY BLADDER

PROSTATE

VAS DEFERENS

PENIS

TESTIS

SCROTUM

Fig. 24–1 THE REPRODUCTIVE TRACT OF A MALE MOUSE

by fluids from various glands such as the *seminal vesicles* and *prostates.* In the mouse (but not man) a *coagulating gland* adds its contribution which makes the fluid become a solid plug inside the female. The combined ejaculate (about a teaspoonful in humans) is discharged from the urethral canal of the male *penis* into the vagina of the female. Urine also passes through the urethra but never at the same time as sperm.

**The male hormone.** The hormone which separates men from boys is called *testosterone.* This, too, is derived from the testes but from cells different from those producing sperm. At puberty (about twelve to fourteen years of age in man) testosterone increases in quantity. As a result, the beard starts to grow, the voice lowers, the body becomes more muscular, and an interest in the opposite sex develops.

Testosterone also controls dominance and social order. In chickens the one with the greatest supply of hormone pecks the others. The one with the next greatest supply pecks all but the first chick and so on. Similar to this "pecking order" there is a "butting order" in cows and a "biting order" in mice.

**The female reproductive tract.** Reproductive organs of females are called *ovaries*. Two of these lie deep in the abdomen on the back side (Fig. 23–1). At puberty, ovaries grow and commence manufacturing *eggs*. In mammals these are barely visible or microscopic in size, but in birds, of course, they are large and edible.

Differences exist in frequency of egg release. The mouse, for instance, produces a new supply every four or five days. Human females release one egg about once a month. Mice and most animals mate only at the time of egg release. Human females may have intercourse at any time, but there are only two or three days during the month when they may become pregnant.

An egg passes from the ovary through the *oviduct* where it is fertilized if sperm is present. The fertile egg then enters and implants itself in the *uterus* where it gradually develops until birth (Chapter 1). If, as usually happens, the egg is not fertilized, it degenerates.

During each reproductive cycle the uterus increases its blood supply and makes other changes suitable for implantation of the egg. The cycle in women is accompanied by a monthly periodic bleeding called *menstruation,* except during pregnancy.

**The female hormone.** *Estrogen,* one of several female hormones, is derived from the ovaries. Increasing amounts appear at puberty to transform girls into physically mature women. At this time the breasts enlarge and the hips broaden. The female is now capable of mating and becoming pregnant.

**Castration and changing sex.** *Castration* (testes removal) of male farm animals is a rather common practice. The result is a steer instead of a bull or a capon instead of a rooster. Such animals put on weight easily and have more tender, edible meat. They have not actually changed sex, but they have lost their ability to reproduce.

Sex operations in chickens sometimes have strange consequences. Only the left ovary of a hen develops to lay eggs; the other is present but degenerate. If the functional left ovary of a chick is removed within twenty days of hatching, the female becomes a full-fledged rooster with all rights and privileges! The right rudimentary ovary becomes a testis. If the operation is performed after twenty days, the right ovary develops and the chick remains a hen.

## SURGICAL REMOVAL OF MOUSE TESTES

Place a male mouse in a small closed jar or inverted beaker containing ether-soaked cotton. Remove the animal when he has just passed out and place him on his back. Prevent a return to consciousness by placing an ether cone at his nose. This is a device formed by rolling heavy paper into a cone shape with the tip cut off. Keep ether-soaked cotton inside. Take care not to overetherize the mouse. Keep him etherized just enough to prevent pain.

Apply rubbing alcohol liberally to the scrotum to prevent postoperative infection. Castrate by first making a one-fourth inch long incision with scissors along the mid-line of the scrotum between the penis and the anus. A thin layer of transparent connective tissue will be found over each of the two testes. Puncture this covering and draw one testis out with narrow forceps (Fig. 24–2). (In some cases the testes will not be

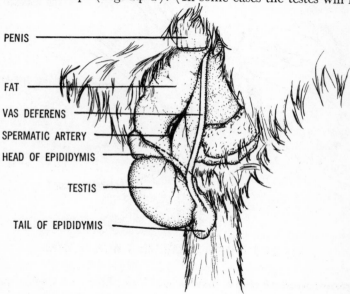

PENIS

FAT

VAS DEFERENS

SPERMATIC ARTERY

HEAD OF EPIDIDYMIS

TESTIS

TAIL OF EPIDIDYMIS

Fig. 24–2 REMOVAL OF A MOUSE TESTIS

in the scrotum. Press with thumbs on the lower abdomen to make them descend.) As the testis is pulled out, it will be followed by a string of fatty tissue containing blood vessels and the vas deferens. Tie off the vessels with the fat to prevent bleeding; then cut free the gonad by sectioning fat near the tie, between the knot and the testis. Remove the second testis in a manner similar to the first.

The scrotum must now be sewed back together. Check Fig. 24–3 for the method of tying a square knot. Use three (or more if necessary) ties to close the opening. These can be done with the fingers but the use of forceps is faster, once the technique is mastered. The operation is now complete. Swab the scrotum again with alcohol. Return the mouse to a warm, clean cage in which there are no other mice. Recovery will be rapid if the operation was properly performed.

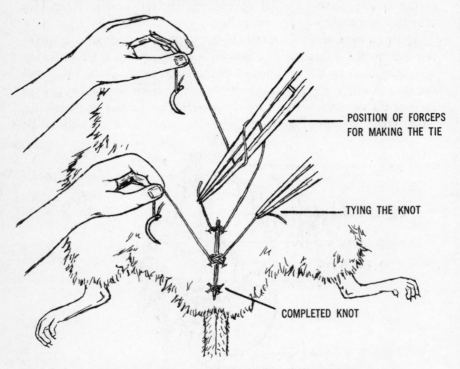

POSITION OF FORCEPS
FOR MAKING THE TIE

TYING THE KNOT

COMPLETED KNOT

Fig. 24–3 TYING A SQUARE KNOT WITH FORCEPS

**Degeneration of male structures.** Wait about one week. Anesthetize first your castrate, then a normal male mouse. Open the abdomens of both. Pull intestines to one side. Expose the paired, creamy-white seminal vesicles and the darker, less opaque, closely attached coagulating glands (Fig. 24–1). Compare these structures, noting their diminutive size in the experimental mouse. Prostates show the same effect. It will be apparent that the testes and testosterone are essential for maintaining a normal reproductive tract. Now sew the abdominal walls back together and allow your animals to recover.

## OTHER THINGS TO DO

Castration is an especially good operation for the beginning surgeon. It is relatively simple and well tolerated by most animals. It may take one-half to one hour when first tried, but the time decreases rapidly with successive attempts. Mice are appropriate since they handle easily and are resistant to infection.

As a second operation, you may undertake the slightly more difficult removal of ovaries. Make a small skin incision on one side of the back of an anesthetized female mouse, midway between fore and hind limbs and about one-fourth inch from the backbone. A spherical, pinkish-colored ovary is usually visible beneath the semitransparent covering of the abdomen (Fig. 23–1). Cut through the covering and pull the ovary to the surface. Pinch off the oviduct with forceps and cut the gonad free. Close the incision. Repeat this procedure on the opposite side. The animal is now *ovariectomized*. Her reproductive tract will diminish in size, and she will no longer come into heat.

As a general rule, you should examine an animal's anatomy before attempting surgery. For castration, you may feel the testes, thus eliminating the need to see them. For ovariectomy and removal of other glands, you should study preserved specimens and refer to a book of methodology such as J. Markowitz, J. Archibald, and H. G. Downie, *Experimental Surgery*, The Williams and Wilkins Company, Baltimore, 1954. Seek supervision of operative technique if at all possible.

If you want to show the effects of a hormone without resorting to surgery, this may be done with chicks. Their combs grow rapidly under the influence of testosterone, in a manner similar to the sprouting beards of young men. Use an ether or corn-oil solution containing 100 micrograms of testosterone per 0.1 ml. Apply this quantity directly to the comb of several-day-old animals once daily for one week. Compare their large, red combs with those of normal chicks.

# Skeleton, Muscles, and Energy

## 25
## BONES OF MEN AND DINOSAURS

### Materials.
1. A kit of small plastic dinosaur bones
2. Plastic cement

**The age of dinosaurs.** North America was a hot, humid, tropical swampland at the start of the Mesozoic era 200,000,000 years ago. No mammals yet walked the earth. Ferns, horsetails, and other primitive plants were the only vegetation. In this environment the dinosaurs developed and ruled for over 100,000,000 years . . . then disappeared. Only a few of their reptilian kin have survived into recent times.

Some dinosaurs were small; some were large. Among the largest was *Brontosaurus,* the thunder lizard. Stout, tree-thick legs supported this creature's thirty-five ton weight and seventy foot length. Despite his great size he was a peaceful plant-eater who spent most of his time at rest in shallow water. *Stegosaurus* was also a vegetarian and a contemporary of Brontosaurus. This beast was heavily armored and provided with a spiked tail for defense. The tail swung a telling blow against his adversaries. *Tyrannosaurus rex,* the tyrant king of the dinosaurs, was the most fierce of all land animals, past or present (Fig. 25–1). He was a flesh-eater, twenty feet tall and fifty feet long. Tyrannosaurus frequently attacked the plant-eater, *Triceratops,* who was likewise no weakling. Triceratops' defense consisted of three horns, two of which were long and pointed. The neck was protected by a huge flaring collar of bone.

The age of dinosaurs was one of much diversity. Even flying reptiles eventually appeared. These cold-blooded creatures had immense wings well adapted for soaring but poorly adapted for flight. *Pterodactyl* was one of the reptiles which took to the air in the late Mesozoic era.

Mammal-like reptiles were present even somewhat before the time of dinosaurs. They evolved as warm-blooded, hairy creatures during the 125,000,000-year reign of the giants. Man himself is a much later evolutionary development. He has been on earth for only one million years, but his progress during this brief period has been greater than that of any animal which has preceded him.

### Fig. 25–1 THE SKELETON OF TYRANNOSAURUS
Drawn from an Ideal Toy Corporation model

**Structure and function of bone.** Both dinosaurs and men have an internal skeleton with many striking similarities. In each case we find a long, slightly flexible backbone composed of numerous separate units called vertebrae, a hipbone and shoulder girdle from which the legs and arms extend, and a strong protective skull. The duplication goes further than this, however, for in general we find matches for each separate piece. Thus scientists can and do give dinosaur bones the same names as the bones in humans. With certain limitations this is true of the other vertebrates as well, whether fish, amphibian, reptile, bird, or mammal.

The architecture within bones also reveals close resemblances. To illustrate the basic construction, a longitudinal section of the femur (thigh bone) of a human is shown in Fig. 25-2. The outer covering is one of solid, so-called *compact bone*. The inside portion consists of a bony network having a spongy appearance. Careful examination reveals that this network follows the lines of stress imposed by standing and

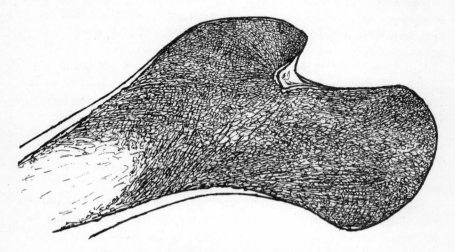

Fig. 25-2 STRUCTURE WITHIN THE HUMAN FEMUR

walking. In the femur, as in many other bones, there is a hollowed-out central area. This cavity and the adjacent spongy network contain a soft tissue called *marrow,* which manufactures red and white blood cells.

Bone contains living cells imbedded in a hard, non-living framework. The living cells are supplied with minute blood and lymph vessels and nerves. The non-living framework is about one-third cartilage and one-half mineral; the remainder is water. Cartilage is a tough, jellylike material containing many small fibers. The mineral content is mostly calcium and phosphorus. Bones of the body are bound together by ligaments of tough connective tissue.

## BUILDING A DINOSAUR

Excellent kits can be obtained for assembling skeletons of various dinosaurs. These can be purchased at local hobby shops or from the Ideal Toy Corporation, Hollis 23, New York. Get a kit and construct your own dinosaur. Use a quick-drying plastic cement for holding the pieces in place. The manufacturer's literature will give the names of the bones. Compare your dinosaur with Fig. 25–3 to discover the similarities of human and dinosaur skeletons.

**Examining your skeleton.** Since everyone carries his own skeleton, we each have an excellent model for study. Feel out the various bones, where possible, and compare with the human skeleton in Fig. 25–3 or with a real human skeleton if such is available.

The bones of both the toes and fingers are called *phalanges*. In the foot proper the phalanges attach to *metatarsals;* in the hand they connect with *metacarpals*. Bones of the ankle are *tarsals* and bones of the wrist are *carpals*.

Feel the shinbone of the lower leg. This is the *tibia*. It is aided in supporting the body by a narrower bone, the *fibula*. The cap of bone at the knee is the *patella*. The upper leg has only one large bone, the *femur*. It connects to the hip by a ball-and-socket type joint.

The hipbone is one large fused structure in adult humans, but is separated in three parts in children. These are called the *pubis* (in front), *ischium* (in back), and *ilium* (the flared bone which projects outward beneath the waistline).

The backbone consists of many separate smaller bones called *vertebrae*. Twelve paired *ribs* are attached to the sides of the vertebrae in the chest. Cartilages extend from these ribs to the breastbone, or *sternum* at the center of the chest.

The collarbone, or *clavicle* extends from the sternum into the shoulder. Here it joins the shoulder blade, or *scapula*.

The *humerus* is the bone of the upper arm. Bones in the lower arm are the *radius* and *ulna*.

The *skull* attaches to vertebrae in the neck. Note projections and depressions of the skull in Fig. 25–3. See if you can detect these on your own head.

## OTHER THINGS TO DO

Skulls and skeletons hold an indefinable allure for many of us humans. If you are among those who appreciate their beauty and instructional value, you may make a collection of your own. Start with the head of some animal you have hunted or found dead at the side of the road. Remove the eyes, the brain, and as much flesh as possible. Put the cleaned head in water in a warm room and allow the remaining meat to decompose for about one week. At the end of this time, rinse the

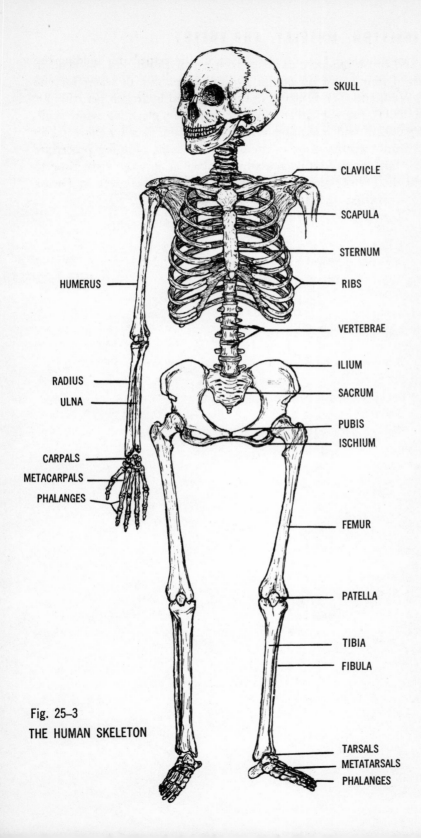

SKULL

CLAVICLE

SCAPULA

STERNUM

RIBS

HUMERUS

VERTEBRAE

ILIUM

RADIUS

SACRUM

ULNA

PUBIS

ISCHIUM

CARPALS

METACARPALS

PHALANGES

FEMUR

PATELLA

TIBIA

FIBULA

Fig. 25–3
THE HUMAN SKELETON

TARSALS

METATARSALS

PHALANGES

skull and brush off loose particles with a stiff brush. Put the skull in a bath of four grams of sodium hydroxide per liter of water for one hour. Wash and then bleach it in three per cent hydrogen peroxide for ten hours. You now have an attractive, durable, gleaming white skull.

Preparation and mounting of whole skeletons is a bit more tricky but certainly worthy of your attention. The same cleaning procedure is used, but decomposition must be stopped at just the right time to prevent the loss of ligaments. The complete method is given in Turtox Service Leaflet No. 9, "How to make skeletons."

# 26

# CONTRACTING FROG LEGS

**Materials.**
1. Frogs
2. Batteries ( 1½ volts, No. 6 )
3. Small pieces of insulated copper wire

**Muscle—what it is and where it is.** Most of us realize that muscles comprise a very large part of our bodies. Frequently we try to alter our muscles for strength and beauty. Weight lifters strive for bulging arm and shoulder muscles. Runners strengthen their legs. Many middle-aged people exercise to dispose of "bay windows" by developing the abdominal muscles. The muscles mentioned here are *skeletal* muscles. They attach and insert on bones and, by contraction, enable us to sit, stand, and move about.

There are two other important types of muscle—smooth and cardiac. *Smooth* muscle is found in the stomach and intestines and in several other organs of the body. The muscular wall of the digestive canal is continually contracting and relaxing. By this means it mixes food with digestive juices and pushes wastes into and out of the large intestine. Other smooth muscle, found in blood vessels, helps regulate the speed and force of circulation.

*Cardiac* muscle is unique in that it can be found in only one structure—the heart. This small pump moves almost 4000 gallons of blood daily, with no vacations, for the duration of a man's life. An equally remarkable machine cannot be found outside the body.

**Muscle tone.** The pitcher always "warms up" before starting his game. Most athletes follow the same practice. Why bother? Mainly because it relaxes tense muscles; it reduces their tone.

*Tone* can be defined as a continual state of partial contraction. The extent of contraction varies with activity, being least in sleep, more while sitting, and more yet while standing. Cold and excitement are other factors which increase muscle tone. Many of us have experienced extra-taut muscles while sitting in the football stadium at a late fall game.

Smooth muscle also must remain partially contracted. With decreased tone in the intestines, food and wastes move slowly. Constipation results. A reduction of tone in blood vessels causes blushing and fainting. If there were no tone at all, the individual would die of shock.

**Muscle protein and what makes it contract.** Muscle is a marvelous material. Frequently and silently it transforms from a soft jelly to a hardened, contracted mass which lifts up to 1000 times its own weight. Sometimes it moves slowly and regularly, as in the heart. At other times it contracts hundreds of times per second, as in the wing muscles of certain insects. In any event, its performance warrants close attention.

What is this contractile unit which operates so forcefully, and where does it get its energy? To answer the first part of the question, we retreat into history to the laboratory of a German scientist, Willie Kühne. The year is 1868; he has just obtained a muscle extract which he calls *myosin*. This is an important discovery. Kühne's myosin is the actual contractile material of muscle, but we now know that it is composed of two proteins rather than one. The combination has been re-christened *actomyosin*.

In 1934, another German, Hans Weber, discovered a way to squirt this protein material into water and precipitate it as a thread. The Hungarian-born American scientist, Albert Szent-Györgyi, got actomyosin by this same method in 1941, but he went one remarkable step further. He put his protein fibers into a potassium salt bath which also contained *adenosinetriphosphate* (abbreviated *ATP*). The fibers contracted! Outside the body, Szent-Györgyi had duplicated with chemicals what the body had been doing internally for aeons.

The energy-rich ATP, present in all living systems, can do its job temporarily even when no oxygen is present. This point would have surprised the old-time physiologists, for they knew only the final step in a series of reactions which enable muscle to contract. They knew that a carbohydrate called *glycogen* broke down to *glucose* and then to *lactic acid*. Following this, *oxygen* from the lungs and blood converted the lactic acid back to glucose and the glucose to glycogen; thus the body's battery was recharged and ready for more work. We still recognize the necessity of these reactions, but we give equal credit to ATP breakdown, which allows muscle contractions even in an atmosphere of pure nitrogen. Ultimately, however, the muscle will cease performing unless revived by a good supply of oxygen and glucose.

**Conduction of impulses.** A *stimulus* is some change in the environment which starts an impulse through a nerve and by this means produces muscular contraction. For instance, you are chewing walnuts and bite into a piece of shell (stimulus). A message (impulse) passes to the brain, informing it of this insult. An impulse returning from the brain causes you to move certain muscles forcefully to eject the offending particle.

The impulse which is conducted through nerves and into muscles results from an electrochemical change at each of the tissues. The surfaces of nerve and muscle normally carry a positive charge. Application of a stimulus causes a negative charge to form and travel along the membrane. In short order the negative charge is again replaced by a positive one, and the membrane is back to its normal state (Fig. 26–1).

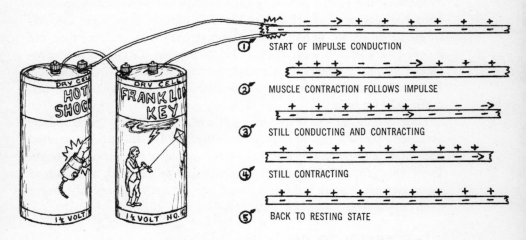

Fig. 26–1 CONDUCTION AND CONTRACTION IN MUSCLE

It is somewhat like burning a trail of gunpowder except that in this case the gunpowder is continually regenerated shortly after being burned.

## STIMULATION OF NERVE AND MUSCLE
Attach two 1½-volt batteries in series and run off copper wires for stimulation (Fig. 26–1). Cut off the head of a frog (Fig. 16–1) and run a dissecting needle down its spinal cord. Remove the skin from the

animal's hind leg, exposing the muscles completely. Locate the *sciatic* nerve on the back side of the thigh between the triceps femoris and semimembranosus muscles and underneath the thin iliofibularis muscle (Fig. 26–2). This can be found by pulling the muscles apart and looking beneath for the white, threadlike nerve.

Gently pull up the sciatic nerve. Stimulate it with the uninsulated ends of the copper wire. A muscle in the lower part of the leg makes a strong contraction. This is the *gastrocnemius* (Fig. 26–2). Remove the stimulators and apply directly to the gastrocnemius. It contracts again. Now place the wires on the triceps femoris, semimembranosus, and iliofibularis muscles and on various other muscles to see what happens.

**Galvanoscopic frog leg.** In the eighteenth century Luigi Galvani first showed that a muscle, by itself, can produce a strong enough current to bring about contraction in a second muscle. This experiment can be repeated exactly as Galvani did it.

Remove the gastrocnemius muscle of the leg which has previously been stimulated. Slice off one end of this muscle. Now strip the skin from the other leg. Loosen a sciatic nerve as before, but this time cut it free (leaving it as long as possible) at the hip. Leave the nerve attached to the gastrocnemius muscle and remove both from the leg. Do this by first disconnecting the gastrocnemius at the ankle and then cutting the leg bones.

Look at Fig. 26–3. Place the freshly obtained nerve (with muscle attached) against the injured or cut muscle. Do this at the injured and intact ends simultaneously. A circuit is created between the negatively charged inner surface and the positively charged, undamaged outer surface. The impulse generated is conducted through the nerve to its muscle which then contracts.

## OTHER THINGS TO DO

Galvani discovered another curious way to get little leaps from frog legs. For a modified repetition of his second method, you must first obtain some zinc and copper wire. Use a double-pithed frog, perhaps one which has just been studied in some other experiment. Skin the hind legs and open the abdomen. Remove the intestines and other organs to expose spinal nerves seven, eight, nine, and ten (Fig. 15–1) which continue into the leg as the sciatic nerve. Loop an uninsulated copper wire under the spinal nerves on both sides of the backbone. Suspend the frog in air. Attach a strip of zinc wire or metal to one end of the copper wire and touch this repeatedly against the animal's

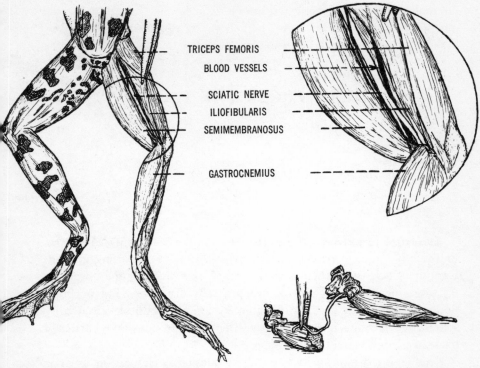

TRICEPS FEMORIS

BLOOD VESSELS

SCIATIC NERVE

ILIOFIBULARIS

SEMIMEMBRANOSUS

GASTROCNEMIUS

Fig. 26-2 SCIATIC NERVE AND MUSCLES

Fig. 26-3 CURRENT OF INJURY
CAUSES CONTRACTION

bare muscle. The legs jump apart in a most animated manner. The stimulus is the result of two metals being in contact with a moist conductor, the muscle-nerve preparation. Thus a current is generated in a way similar to current production in a battery.

Human muscle contractions are studied with devices called *ergographs*. Simple, inexpensive finger ergographs are available from suppliers of physiological apparatus. In these, the finger pushes against a lever which records the extent of movement and the time until fatigue. If the rate of contraction is rapid or if the blood supply to the hand is blocked, exhaustion will be hastened. Hypnotized subjects can be directed to work their fingers for a vastly longer time than normal subjects. We seem to have almost unlimited reserves of power if we could but use them and ignore subjective feelings of tiredness.

# 27

# HEAT FROM THE HAND

**Materials.**
  1. Four 1000-milliliter beakers
  2. Thermometer
  3. Ice

**Exposure to extreme temperatures.** In the wastelands of Australia there is a race of people who sleep naked on near-freezing ground. Campfires help heat their bodies; yet, if any civilized man were to try the same feat, he would be exceptionally distressed. The acclimation of the natives is made possible by an ultrasensitive circulatory system. Blood drains from the skin during the night, leaving a barrier of tissue insulation better than cork.

Even civilized man has a remarkably adaptable circulation. Five or six times as much heat is lost from the body when the skin vessels are maximally dilated (large diameter) as when they are maximally constricted (small diameter). During exposure to cold, warm blood is rapidly removed from the skin and diverted to the interior.

The hands and feet suffer most from this diversion of the circulation. The feet get cold first, then the hands. Fortunately, they do not remain cold for long durations of time. Periods of cooling are alternated with brief periods of rewarming, particularly if the cold is severe. Although the exposed part is not heated to its original temperature by this occasional flushing of the skin, there is enough warmth to give limited protection against frostbite. Birds must especially depend on this mechanism when they stand barefooted on frigid winter snow.

The brain is the "thermostat" which turns the skin's warming blood supply on and off. Low temperatures arouse this reaction, as well as another, which is shivering. Our muscles tighten, our limbs shake, our teeth chatter as temperatures go down. Shivering increases the body's heat production four- or fivefold if sufficiently violent.

Man's body also adapts to heat. Blood flow increases in the skin with a resulting increase in heat loss. The most important means of cooling the body is sweat evaporation. As much as ten liters (two and one-half gallons) of water per day are lost by men working in hot, dry climates.

**Heat production at rest.** The units for measuring heat production and loss are the kilocalorie (kcal. or Cal.) and calorie (cal.). A *kilocalorie* is the amount of heat required to raise one liter of water one degree centigrade. This is the exact equivalent of the Calorie, more familiar to laymen because of its use by dietitions. The smaller *calorie* (not captialized) is the amount of heat which raises one milliliter of water one degree centigrade, in other words, one thousandth of a kilocalorie.

An adult human at rest produces about 1600 kcal. of heat per day. This is called basal, or resting heat production. The usual daily food intake of adults contains about 3000 kcal. The difference between 1600 and 3000 kcal. is explained by activity differences. The adult human rests during only part of his day. During the remainder he sits, stands, walks, or performs other exercises which increase his heat production and correspondingly increase his food caloric requirement.

**Heat production during exercise.** Exercise is the most important of all means of increasing heat above the basal level. Sitting raises the metabolism twenty-five per cent. Walking triples the basal heat. Running ten miles per hour increases the metabolic rate by a factor of twelve (Fig. 27–1). Exercising specific portions of the body, such as a hand, will produce local increases in tissue oxygen consumption and corresponding increases in heat production.

**The mechanisms of heat transfer.** There are four basic methods of losing heat: (1) radiation, (2) conduction, (3) convection, and (4) evaporation. Heat can also be gained by each of these methods except evaporation (Fig. 27–2).

*Radiation* is the transfer of heat across space by electromagnetic waves. Heat radiates from the animal body to a cold wall. The body receives heat by radiation from the sun or a fire.

*Conduction* is the direct transfer of heat from one molecule to another. Heat is conducted from one's own seat to the cold concrete seat of a football stadium. Heat gain occurs by conduction when one places a hand against hot water pipes.

*Convection* is the transfer of heat through currents of gas or liquid. Hot air rises while cool air descends. Warm vapors rise directly from the skin and are exhaled from the lungs into the atmosphere.

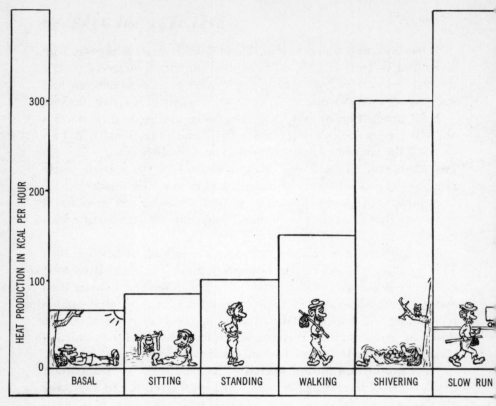

Fig. 27-1 CHANGES IN HEAT PRODUCTION WITH ACTIVITY

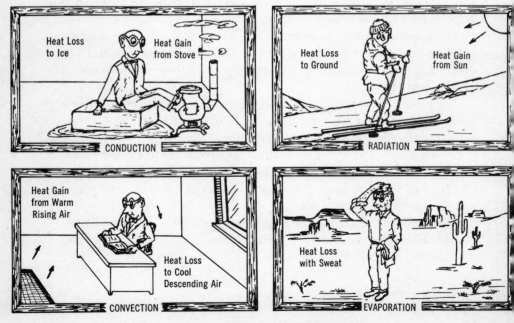

Fig. 27-2 WAYS TO GAIN OR LOSE HEAT

*Evaporation* is heat lost in the change of water to water vapor, such as occurs when one sweats. Although invisible, some water is lost and consequent cooling occurs by this means at all times. Sweating, however, increases the heat loss very considerably in hot climates.

## DETERMINING HEAT LOSS FROM THE HAND

This experiment will show: (1) heat loss from a hand plunged in cold water, (2) the reduced heat loss from a hand, previously exposed to cold, and (3) the increased heat production and heat loss from a hand in motion.

Obtain four 1000-milliliter beakers (or similar containers). Place enough water in each to cover entirely your immersed hand. About 500 milliliters should prove adequate. This water must be at 10°C. at the beginning of each of the following tests (Fig. 27–3).

Fig. 27–3 POSITION OF HAND FOR COLD TEST

Use the first beaker to obtain a normal record of heat loss. Place in this beaker a thermometer and your hand. Stir the water frequently to distribute heat. Record the temperature rise of the water at minute intervals for five minutes.

Remove your hand from the first beaker and immediately immerse it in the second beaker at 10°C. Take temperature records at minute intervals for five minutes. The smaller rise in water temperature can be attributed to constriction of blood vessels and a reduction of skin temperature which occurred during the initial experiment.

Wait thirty minutes or preferably longer before performing a third test on the effects of exercise. Rewarm the hand to its normal temperature by jumping around a bit. When the hand is again warm and comfortable, place it in another beaker with water at 10°C. Exercise the hand by moving all fingers rapidly while taking care not to spill water from the beaker. Determine the temperature rise at minute intervals for five minutes. Note that exercise augments heat loss. Similar effects can be demonstrated when the entire body is exercised.

Place only a thermometer in the fourth beaker of 10°C. water. Note the very slow rise in temperature at minute intervals for five minutes. The difference between this beaker and the others is the corrected rise in water temperature attributable to the hand.

Compare temperature rises during the various minute intervals. At certain times this rise is much greater than at others. This illustrates that blood vessels alternately constrict and dilate to protect an exposed part. Increased blood supply increases heat loss while a decreased supply decreases the loss (Fig. 27–4).

## OTHER THINGS TO DO

Most of us have a regular pattern of activity in the daytime, followed by sleep at night. Upon arising and shortly before retiring, we are not quite so alert as we are in the middle of the day. Biologists have shown that this activity is closely related to body temperature. In the early morning hours our temperatures are about one degree F. lower than in the afternoon. If you have a clinical thermometer, take your oral temperature first thing in the morning and at several regular intervals throughout the day. Is your peak reached in the afternoon? Is the pattern about the same on successive days?

Sweat-soaked shirts are a common sight among physical laborers on hot, humid days. You, too, have probably perspired abundantly while mowing the lawn or hoeing the garden. On these days your liquid con-

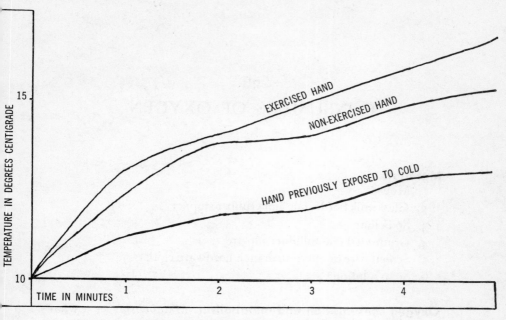

Fig. 27-4 TEMPERATURE RISE OF WATER WITH HAND IMMERSED

sumption must also rise to balance the water loss. Record, during two or three cool and inactive days, the amount of water, milk, and other liquids which you drink. Do the same for a comparable period of hot, dry weather during which you put in several hours of hard work each day. Notice any difference?

# 28

# CONSUMERS OF OXYGEN

**Materials.**
1. Mouse
2. Glass milk bottle, one-hole rubber stopper
3. Soda lime
4. Graduated one-milliliter pipette
5. Screen wire or one-fourth inch hardware cloth
6. Soap solution

**Oxygen consumption and metabolism.** *Metabolism* . . . what's that? Energy for movement is obtained through metabolism. Heat to warm the body comes from the same source. How does it happen? Complex carbohydrates, proteins, and fats break down in the body. During this process, energy and heat are released. To rebuild these materials, so vital for activity, *oxygen* must be added. All of these occurrences are referred to as metabolism, and they can be determined directly or indirectly.

The *indirect* measurement of metabolism, widely used in medicine, is based on oxygen consumption. The subject breathes into and out of a closed vessel of oxygen, gradually exhausting the supply. Carbon dioxide from the body accumulates but is rapidly absorbed by some agent such as *soda lime*. A measure of the oxygen decrease is an indirect measure of metabolism, since 4.8 Calories of heat are released for every liter of oxygen consumed.

The very accurate but unhandy *direct* determination of metabolism calls for a closed chamber into which a man or other animal is placed. Water, circulated in pipes surrounding the chamber, is warmed by the animal's body. Sweat is absorbed and weighed. By knowing the temperature rise of the water and the evaporative cooling power of his perspiration, the total metabolism can be readily calculated.

**Variations in oxygen consumption.** Big animals use more oxygen than little animals, a relation easily surmised. Oxygen consumption, however, is proportional to the surface of an animal rather than his weight. A mouse (with large surface area relative to weight) has a much higher metabolism *per square meter* than does a man and must consume large quantities of heat-producing nutrients. An even tinier animal, the shrew, daily eats his weight in food to keep warm and alive.

"Cold-blooded" animals such as frogs and lizards have very low metabolisms. They expend no energy for warming their bodies; it all goes for work. They sometimes exist for long periods of time without nourishment.

Exercise and shivering have been previously mentioned (Fig. 27–1) as causing tremendous increases in heat production and, therefore, oxygen consumed.

**Metabolism and disease.** A patient comes in complaining of fatigue and cold feet. His skin is thick and puffy, hair dry and brittle. The physician asks him to return after a good night's sleep and take a metabolism test. A resting metabolic rate thirty per cent below normal suggests a thyroid glandular deficiency and treatment with thyroid tablets.

Many diseases can be partially diagnosed by measuring oxygen consumption. Thyroid, pituitary, and adrenal deficiencies, as well as malnutrition, cause reductions in resting metabolism. In fevers and certain blood diseases the metabolism is raised.

**Conditions for a metabolism test.**    Metabolism tests must be performed exactingly to be of any value. Exertion or excitement will invariably alter the values. For standard comparison the measurements are taken only on patients at rest who have not had a meal in the past twelve to eighteen hours. The value thus obtained is called a *basal metabolic rate*.

## MEASURING THE OXYGEN CONSUMPTION OF A MOUSE

Select a square-sided milk bottle or other wide-mouth bottle having one quart or greater capacity. Pour in a generous layer of soda lime and turn it on its side (Fig. 28–1). Procure a one-hole rubber stopper which fits the mouth. Insert the end of a graduated one-milliliter pipette into this hole.

The mouse which is put into the bottle should be held in a closed wire cylinder which will not permit him to turn around. This may be constructed from screen wire or quarter-inch hardware cloth. Attach this cage to a strip of cardboard which lies on top of the soda lime.

Now you are ready! Form a soap bubble at one end of the pipette. The dime-store solution from which children blow soap bubbles is ideal for this purpose. The bubble descends slowly as the mouse breathes and uses oxygen. Soda lime prevents the accumulation of carbon dioxide which would halt the bubble's descent. Record the time taken by the bubble in traveling one milliliter. Repeat two or three times and average the values. Calculate from this the oxygen consumed in one minute and how much heat this represents. Remember that one liter of oxygen equals 4.8 Calories and that there are 1000 milliliters in one liter.

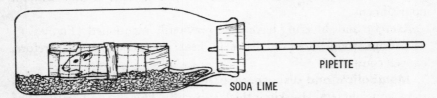

PIPETTE

SODA LIME

Fig. 28–1 APPARATUS FOR MEASURING METABOLISM

This determination, performed after the mouse is put in, will not give a basal metabolic rate. The mouse is excited and fearful and will move about constantly. His oxygen consumption will be high. Wait half an hour after these first measurements and repeat the tests again. Your mouse is probably quieter now and better acquainted with his surroundings. Does he consume oxygen less rapidly?

## OTHER THINGS TO DO

Even very small and cold-blooded animals are oxygen consumers and will not last forever without this vital gas. The validity of this can be shown by sealing the little animals permanently apart from our world.

Obtain two test tubes made of soft glass (not Pyrex). Heat in a Bunsen flame and draw each tube out so that only a narrow opening is left in the center. Allow these to cool. Pour filtered aquarium or pond water into the bottom of the tubes and drop a small snail through the constricted portion into the water of each. To one of the tubes add pieces of aquarium plants to serve as oxygen generators. Now heat and seal off (by pulling apart) the narrow portion of the tube, being careful to keep the flame away from the water. Place both of these "microaquaria" in a well-lighted part of the room but not in direct sunlight. Which snail lives the longest? If you want to save time, use rubber stoppers rather than a heat seal to close off tubes containing snails.

The study of closed, balanced aquaria and terraria is an important aspect of modern-day space medicine. Transportation of oxygen tanks to satellites and moon stations is not practical for permanent installations. The metabolic needs of man can be satisfied by growing algae (miscroscopic green plants) in strong light. Algae are especially good for producing large quantities of oxygen. Carbon dioxide, a waste gas of man, is utilized by the algae. If you want to investigate this problem, use mice or other mammals in place of snails. Several square feet of the rapidly growing alga, chlorella, should support the life of one mouse. For details, check M. F. Lee, J. P. Henry, and E. R. Ballinger, "Basic requirements for survival of mice in a sealed atmosphere," *Journal of Aviation Medicine,* 25:399, 1954, and J. Myers. "Basic remarks on the use of plants as biological gas exchangers in a closed system," *Journal of Aviation Medicine,* 25: 407, 1954.

# Digestion and Nutrition

## 29
## THE GREAT FOOD TUNNEL

**Materials.**
1. Frog
2. Dissecting instruments
3. Sodium chloride (table salt)
4. One per cent pilocarpine
5. 1 : 1000 Adrenalin

**Dr. Beaumont and Saint Martin.** One summer day in 1822 a gun accidentally belched its contents into the stomach of Alexis St. Martin, a fur trapper at Fort Mackinac, Wisconsin. The fort's surgeon, William Beaumont, was summoned at once. He repaired the wound, but predicted the young man would die within thirty-six hours.

The rugged St. Martin survived but developed a permanent opening in his stomach, with a natural flap of tissue to cover it. Dr. Beaumont hired the man as his servant and soon after made some remarkable observations.

Into this opening Beaumont placed bread, peering inside to see what happened. The stomach wall immediately reddened in color and small drops of gastric juice formed. Gradually the bread dissolved and digested until nothing was left. Continuing, he added meat, fat, bone, and did other curious experiments with his "human test tube." From these he learned that fat digests slowly, that anger halts gastric-juice formation, that the juice forms in proportion to food intake, that hydrochloric acid is one of the important digestive secretions, that excess food will not dissolve, and that the stomach is usually empty within three to four hours after a meal.

Dr. Beaumont continued his experiments for years but not without difficulties. St. Martin disappeared frequently and was somewhat addicted to alcohol. He finally left for good. Beaumont persevered and in 1833 published a book of results which is still read by medical men the world over.

**The passage of food through the great tunnel.** A mouthful of food is generally chewed and wetted with saliva before commencing its slippery journey down the *esophagus* and into the *stomach* (Fig. 29–1). Within the stomach it is gently churned and mingled with hydrochloric acid and enzymes of the gastric juice.

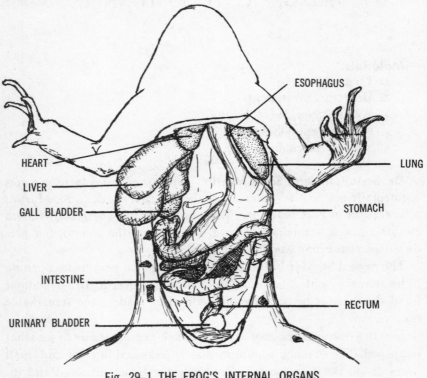

Fig. 29–1 THE FROG'S INTERNAL ORGANS

*Enzymes* are substances inside the body which promote some chemical reaction. Those of the stomach and intestines split complex foods (*carbohydrates, fats,* and *proteins*) into simpler foods (simple *sugars, fatty acids,* and *amino acids*) which are absorbable. The total process in all parts of the tract is called *digestion*.

Foods stay in the stomach for only a few hours and subsequently pass into the *small intestine*. Most of the digestive process and the absorption of foods occurs here. Parts of the food are not digested, but pass into the large intestine where the water is removed. The resultant semisolid waste mass, called *feces*, is eliminated through the rectum.

**Peristalsis—a motion of the tunnel.** Nutrient-splitting enzymes cannot penetrate the center of the food mass unless there is movement of the gastrointestinal tract. This movement is called *peristalsis*. It provides a continual wavelike churning of one's digestibles. The waves of contraction in the stomach and intestinal walls can be divided into two types which usually occur at the same time (Fig. 29–2):

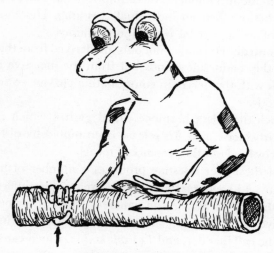

Fig. 29–2 THE TWO TYPES OF PERISTALSIS

1. A narrowing of the diameter of the tract. This occurs at various intervals along the tract but does not push the contents forward. It only mixes the food with enzymes.
2. Waves which pass lengthwise from stomach to intestines to rectum. There is contraction of one part of the tube followed by contraction of another part just in front, then relaxation of the originally contracted segment. This milking motion pushes food and wastes through the tract.

**Nerve control of motion and secretion.** Peristalsis and the release of enzymes are both regulated by the autonomic nervous system consisting of sympathetic and parasympathetic nerves. The sympathetic nerves to the gastrointestinal canal are called *splachnics.* The parasympathetic nerves are the *vagi* (singular, vagus). The vagi also have branches to the heart and lungs.

During exercise and emotional situations (such as the anger of St. Martin), sympathetic nerves respond. They release a substance called *epinephrine* (Adrenalin) which inhibits secretion of digestive enzymes and peristalsis. When an individual is nervous or excited, impulses are especially frequent in these nerves. At such times food is not properly digested, and sometimes the person complains of an "upset" stomach.

Stimulation of parasympathetic nerves releases *acetylcholine* (*ACH*). ACH causes an increased secretion in the stomach and intestines and an increase in mobility. Nerve impulses are most frequent in the parasympathetics when an individual is resting. Digestion is best when activity following a meal is not too strenuous.

**Hormonal control.** Hormones not only are derived from the thyroid, adrenals, and other endocrine glands but from the digestive glands as well. They work with the nerves in co-ordinating enzyme secretion and absorption of foods.

In the stomach there is a hormone called *gastrin* which stimulates secretion of hydrochloric acid. Its release is prompted by distention of the stomach (as by food) or the presence of meats.

The lining of the upper intestine produces a number of hormones. Among these are: (1) *enterocrinin,* which excites intestinal secretion, (2) *secretin,* which is carried to the pancreas where it encourages release of digestive enzymes, (3) *cholecystokinin,* which brings about contraction of the gall bladder, and (4) *villikinine,* which causes churning movements of minute fingerlike projections within the intestine called *villi.* Each of these hormones, in one manner or another, aids the process of digestion.

**How researchers study peristalsis.** One of the really classical experiments on stomach contractions was performed by the Harvard physiologist, Walter Cannon, on his student, Mr. Washburn. Mr. Washburn swallowed a slightly inflated rubber balloon attached to a rubber tube which protruded from his mouth. Every time the student's stomach contracted, a puff of air came through the tube. By connecting the tube to a distensible rubber diaphragm and writing needle, a record was obtained. With this apparatus the two experimenters showed both normal peristalsis and strong contractions which caused hunger pangs.

Cannon's technique is still used in many biology laboratories, but human subjects have generally been replaced by cats and dogs. In another procedure, perhaps more common, a strip of intestine is surgically removed from an animal so that its motion may be directly observed. Rabbits are preferred subjects. Their internal parts are unusually responsive to epinephrine, ACH, and other drugs. The intestinal strip is hooked directly to a lever which records on a rotating smoked drum.

More recently, investigators have developed a capsule with a transistor radio inside it. This is swallowed and its progress followed through the gastrointestinal tract. Peristaltic pressure changes are broadcast to a visual receiver outside the subject's body.

## PERISTALSIS IN THE FROG

Destroy the brain and spinal cord of a frog (Fig. 16–1). Cut open the animal's abdomen, being careful not to damage the intestines. Open wide to expose internal organs completely. Observe the stomach and intestines (Fig. 29–1). Notice the creepingly slow contractions which manipulate food and wastes. This is peristalsis.

Add a few drops of one per cent pilocarpine (one gram of pilocarpine in 100 ml. of water) to the abdominal contents. Pilocarpine directly stimulates cells of the gastrointestinal tract supplied by parasympathetic nerves. It therefore has an action similar to acetylcholine, that of speeding up peristalsis.

Wash off the intestines with frog saline solution (0.7 gm. table salt in 100 ml. of water). Now add to the surface several drops of 0.1 per cent (or 1 : 1000 solution) adrenalin. This relaxes the preparation and inhibits further contractions.

**Abdominal contents of the frog.** Pull the stomach and intestines to one side and locate the remaining structures of the abdominal cavity (Figs. 29–1 and 29–3).

The *pancreas* is an irregular gland found in the connective tissue between the stomach and first part of the small intestine. Very little will be seen of it. This gland produces some of the digestive enzymes which pass by tubes to the small intestine. It also produces insulin, a hormone regulating body sugar.

The *liver* is a massive brown-colored gland located just below the heart and lungs. Foods absorbed from the small intestine are carried to the liver by the blood. Much of this is stored until needed by the body. This gland is also a source of *bile*, a substance essential for the proper digestion of fats.

The *gall bladder* is a green fluid-filled sac embedded beneath the right portion of the liver. It stores bile produced by the liver.

The *spleen* is a dark red spherical body at the underside of the stomach. This gland stores red blood cells. When these are needed, as in exercise, they are released into the blood stream.

The two *kidneys* are located one on each side of the backbone. They are oval, flattened, brown bodies, relatively much larger than those of mammals. Kidneys filter water, wastes, and some simple foods from the blood stream and then reabsorb the foods. Wastes in solution are transported to the *urinary bladder*. The fluid of the bladder (frequently seen emptied and collapsed) is urine.

Cream-colored reproductive organs are found partially covering the kidneys. These are the *testes* of male animals or the larger *ovaries* of females. During reproductive seasons the female's abdominal cavity carries a very full load of eggs generated by her ovaries.

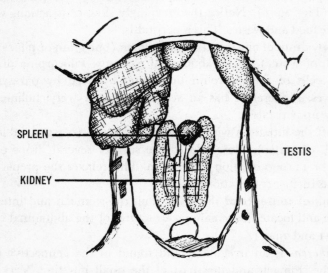

SPLEEN

TESTIS

KIDNEY

Fig. 29–3 THE DEEP ABDOMINAL VISCERA

## OTHER THINGS TO DO

You have now seen how stomach and intestinal walls massage an animal's diet; perhaps you would also like to see what the enzymes do once they have been mixed in. This can be accomplished by first extracting intestinal juices and then testing their potency on bits of various foodstuffs. Hogs make good subjects. Get a one- to two-foot length of hog intestines from a slaughterhouse. Wash and then scrape out the inside lining with a knife. Grind this in a mortar with sand until it breaks into minute pieces. Add five volumes of water and several milliliters of chloroform. Allow your preparation to stand overnight. In the morning, strain the extract through cloth, then try its protein-digesting activity on boiled egg white. Do the same for sucrose, using Benedict's test, described in the following chapter, to show its conversion to the simpler sugar, glucose. If you want more tests of this nature, glance through P. B. Hawk, B. L. Oser, and W.H. Summerson, *Practical Physiological Chemistry,* McGraw-Hill Book Company, Inc., New York, 1954.

# 30

# FUELS AND BODY BUILDERS

**Materials.**
  1. Fruits, potatoes, crackers, and other foods
  2. Iodine, Benedict's solution, nitric acid, ammonium hydroxide, and ether
  3. Test tubes and holder, Bunsen burner, and watch glasses

**A diet of meat.** In 1928 the Arctic explorer, Vilhjalmur Stefansson, and his associate, Karsten Anderson, entered New York City's Bellevue Hospital and began an unusual experiment. For an entire year they agreed to subsist on a diet consisting exclusively of meat. Nutritionists predicted that the subjects would be ill within days or weeks and that the experiment would shortly draw to a close. Stefansson was unimpressed. He had survived without vegetables or dairy products for five out of ten years while traveling in the Arctic. Many Eskimos spend lifetimes under the same restriction.

After numerous carefully supervised tests in the hospital's confines, Stefansson and Anderson returned to their normal activities, but continued eating meat. They took both lean and fat, using their appetites as guides. Like Eskimos, they chose cooked foods, ate brains and hearts but not intestines, and chewed the soft ends of bones. On this regimen they stayed robustly healthy the entire year.

Nutritionists emphasize the value of vegetables, and justly so, but we need not fear our carnivorous desires. Meat is apparently sufficient in calcium and vitamin C, despite notions to the contrary. Eskimo skeletons are adequately calcified (even in non-bone-eaters), and fresh meat has actually cured scurvy, an ailment resulting from an absence of vitamin C.

**Foods and the metabolic pool.** Meat contains protein, one of three chemically distinct types of food. *Protein* is a body builder. It engenders growth and repair of muscles, blood cells, the brain, and other organs.

The other two foods, *fat* and *carbohydrate,* are fuels. They warm the body and make power for movements. Water, vitamins, and minerals are diet necessities but are not ordinarily called foods.

Foods which enter the body do not always retain their identity. They may be converted to something entirely different. For instance, if the cells want energy but receive only building materials, they convert protein to carbohydrate to fulfill their wishes. This method of metabolic interchange does not, however, permit us to thrive on just any old foodstuff. Certain basic items must be in our meals: otherwise, we become ill and die.

**Proteins.** The protein molecule is composed of numerous smaller units called *amino acids,* which couple together like cars of a train. Exactly nine of these are indispensable for the human diet. They are neither made nor converted by the metabolic interchange just mentioned.

Proteins vary in the type, number, and arrangement of amino acids. Both vegetation and animal products contain them. But milk, eggs, and meat have an amino-acid composition which is nearer to that of the human body than, for instance, corn or wheat. For this reason, a small amount of animal food has the same protein nutritional value as a somewhat larger amount of plant food.

It appears that the correct amino acids should be eaten during each meal rather than at different meals. Rats which are fed a diet containing all of the necessary acids at one time make good gains in growth and appearance. But when half are received at one time and half at another time, the animals lose weight.

**Carbohydrates.** Someday man may synthesize his own artificial foods, but until then we must depend on plants to blend carbon dioxide ($CO_2$) and water ($H_2O$) into leaves and fruits. Sunshine is the spark which promotes this carbohydrate $(CH_2O)_n$ building reaction.

Carbohydrates make up the bulk of most diets and, as such, are considered our chief source of energy. They are most plentiful in potatoes, breads, and sweets. When carbohydrates enter the intestinal tract, they split into the smaller-sized *simple sugars* before they are absorbed. Simple sugars are then carried to the liver and muscles where they are reassembled into *glycogen* and stored. When needed, glycogen and sugars chemically decompose and release energy. By-products of this reaction are carbon dioxide and water, the same materials used by plants for cell building. If there are excesses of carbohydrates, they are converted to fats and cause the gaining of weight.

**Fats.** Fats are also composed of carbon, hydrogen, and oxygen, but there is less oxygen than in carbohydrates. This means that more oxygen is needed to "burn" them, and so more calories are obtained. Fats are a combination of *glycerol* and various *fatty acids*. Two of these acids are essential for human health.

**Starvation.** Men have fasted for over thirty days and recovered. Twenty-five per cent of their body weight is lost, but scientists believe as much as forty per cent may be relinquished before death from starvation. During starvation, carbohydrates and fats are the first foods consumed. Later, proteins are used. Lymph tissue and the reproductive tract degenerate quickly. Next the gastrointestinal tract gives in, making the return to food more difficult as meals are poorly digested and absorbed. The brain and heart are least affected.

The study of hunger and its relief is a problem well worth consideration. Estimates of the number of underfed people in the world vary from one third to two thirds of the total population. Surveys of 1951 and 1952 showed that people in the United States consumed about 3200 Calories daily, but the average for India was only 1600 Calories per day. In the Far East, millions slowly die from starvation every year. Disease and epidemics are disproportionately frequent in hunger-stricken areas.

Undoubtedly, famine benefits neither individuals nor populations. Yet researchers have made a surprising discovery. Rats which are fed diets adequate in everything except Calories live considerably longer than their well-fed brothers. How hunger brings about this increase in life span is still unexplained.

## SELECTION OF FOODS FOR TESTING

In this experiment, various foods are to be analyzed for the presence of carbohydrate, fat, and protein. Choose for the first tests foods which definitely contain the desired constituents. Potato will give a good starch test. Honey shows the presence of sugar. Protein will be found in meat or green beans. Butter, margarine, and shortening are mostly fat. Continue by testing other common foods and note which compound or compounds are contained in each.

**Test for fat.** Shake some ether with the food in a test tube. Pour off the ether into a watch glass or petri dish and allow it to evaporate. Grease spots on the watch glass represent fat which dissolved in the ether.

**Test for starch—carbohydrate.** Drop some iodine on a piece of food. A blue-black color indicates the presence of starch. If the brown iodine color remains, there is no starch in the food.

**Test for sugar—another carbohydrate.** Cover a piece of food in a test tube with some Benedict's solution* and boil. If the solution turns a bright orange, much sugar is present. A greenish to reddish color indicates some sugar. If it remains blue, no sugar is present. There is one major exception to this test. Ordinary granulated table sugar (sucrose) will not react positively with Benedict's solution.

**Test for protein.** Place the food in a test tube and cover with concentrated nitric acid. Heat to boiling. Pour off the acid and add a little ammonium hydroxide. A bright yellow color shows lots of protein. Intermediate shades of yellow indicate lesser amounts of protein. (Be careful with these chemicals! Wash off quickly with water if any happens to get on your hands or clothing.)

## OTHER THINGS TO DO

An instructive experiment is described by F. T. Tanner, "Some useful demonstrations in teaching zoology," *Turtox News,* 32:2, January 1954. Partly fill pieces of semipermeable cellophane tubing with (1) boiled starch, (2) the simple sugar, glucose, (3) boiled starch plus saliva, and (4) boiled starch, saliva, and the digestive enzyme maltase. Suspend each piece in a beaker one-third full of water at body temperature (37°C.). Test the water after one hour for sugar, using Benedict's solution, and for starch, using iodine. Large starch molecules will not pass through, just as they will not pass through the intestine before digestion. Saliva does split starch, thanks to a salivary enzyme, and maltase digests it even further. Diffusion is fairly rapid from the starch-splitter tubes, and the tests for sugar are positive.

* Benedict's solution may be purchased ready-made or prepared as follows. Dissolve 17.3 gm. of sodium citrate and 10 gm. of anhydrous sodium carbonate in 70 ml. of warmed distilled water. Filter the resulting fluid. Now dissolve 1.73 gm. of copper sulfate in 10 ml. of water and slowly pour this into the first solution while stirring constantly. Let the mixture cool, then add enough water to make 100 ml. of the final product, the blue-colored Benedict's solution.

# 31

# HOW POOR THE DIET

**Materials.**
1. Three or more young mice weighing eight to fifteen grams
2. Cornstarch, table sugar, lard or bacon drippings, bread, powdered or whole milk, and lettuce
3. A scale for weighing mice (optional but desired)

**Vitality from vitamins.** Of course, many of the nation's poor exist on suboptimal diets. About half pass the day without citrus fruits or tomatoes. Others omit milk and green or yellow vegetables. And yet, money alone does not buy food and health. The rich man's banquet may be starvation disguised. The proper selection of foods, well balanced in vitamins and minerals, rewards both rich and poor with physical and mental fitness.

Why has there been such emphasis on vitamins in recent years? What good are they? What do they do? To answer such questions, we shall begin with the first of the alphabet. *Vitamin A* promotes skin and eye health. A deficiency in this vitamin makes the eyes less sensitive in dim light. Night drivers in such a condition are unable to distinguish road signs and become more prone to accidents.

*Thiamin* ($B_1$), *riboflavin* ($B_2$), and *niacin* are members of the B complex. These vitamins join in *enzyme* combinations which speed the body's chemical reactions and diminish fatigue. Enzymes are active in all cells and so are B vitamins. They affect appetite, digestion, vision, skin, nerves, and mind.

The plague of ancient seamen was *scurvy*. Absent from land for weeks or months, deprived of oranges, lemons, and other fresh fruits, they gradually acquired deficiencies of *vitamin C*. Weakness, swollen, bleeding gums, and loose teeth were the common symptoms. The British Navy, even in the 1700s, used lemons and limes to prevent this condition, acquiring the name "limeys" for their efforts.

*Vitamin D* prevents bowlegs and knock-knees, a condition in children called *rickets*. The vitamin acts by increasing calcium deposits in the bones, thereby increasing skeletal strength. Vitamins *K* for blood clotting, $B_{12}$ and *folic* acid for blood formation, and many others are also important. Interesting stories about these vitamins may be obtained from more detailed texts.

**Minerals.** A survey in 1923 revealed that a great many Michigan school children were tired and inactive. Nearly fifty per cent of them had *goiter,* a thyroid enlargement caused by lack of *iodine.* To revive the weary students, salt manufacturers added iodine to their salt, and families were urged to use it. Health improved with each succeeding year. Special examinations in 1951 showed that slightly over one per cent of the children had goiter, a remarkable change, but typical of what had happened in other iodine-deficient states.

The study and application of mineral knowledge is still advancing. Many communities have not yet made the switch to fluoridated water. Wherever used, one part per million of fluorides in water supplies has reduced dental decay (up to seventy per cent), dental bills, and toothaches.

Milk is sometimes called the perfect food, but even milk must be supplemented with meat and vegetables for best effect. One hundred per cent milk diets are used in experimntal laboratories to produce blood insufficiencies. Milk lacks *copper,* an element which, with *cobalt* and *iron,* stimulates the proper development of red blood cells, the carriers of oxygen.

For strong bones and sound teeth we must have *calcium* and *phosphorus,* minerals often present in less than desirable quantities. Calcium is also essential for blood clotting and maintaining normal heart, nerve, and muscle function.

**Health lost and health regained.** A teen-age girl entered an Alabama nutrition clinic complaining of weakness, nervousness, and loss of weight. When questioned, she explained that a year before she had been overweight and had decided to reduce. For breakfast she had coffee, for lunch, soft drinks and a candy bar, and for supper, a sandwich and cake. The girl lost weight rapidly but began noticing other symptoms. She had burning pains in the stomach and vomiting spells. She heard voices, knocking, and ringing when no one was there. She was afraid of death and already felt cold and dead. She slept very poorly. The physicians gave the girl an injection of thiamin; she was smiling and calm within one hour. Upon switching to a balanced diet, her sickness vanished, her weight returned, and her personality glowed again.

Most diets are not so restricted as the one followed by this particular girl. Still, it is not uncommon to find individuals substituting vitamin-lacking candies, cakes, and carbonated beverages for more wholesome food. This is especially true of between-meal snacks which could consist of health-helping items such as fruit and milk.

Strong, tall, well-proportioned bodies, attractive complexions, and abundant energy are qualities which appeal to most high-school students. Yet, at this age of greatest growth when nutritional requirements are highest, they are least likely to be met. Recent surveys of Iowa teen-agers have shown that only fifteen per cent of the boys and five per cent of the girls completely fulfill the nation's recommended daily allowances for vitamins, minerals, calories, and proteins. Calcium, vitamin C, and iron were most commonly inadequate.

Better choice of food will not startlingly alter health unless it is truly defective. But even slight changes make some difference. In an English boarding school, boys were given an extra pint of milk daily. These boys grew three fourths of an inch taller per year than did comrades who received what had previously been considered a completely adequate diet (Fig. 31–1).

Fig. 31–1 GOOD FOOD BUILDS STRONGER BODIES

## FEEDING DEFICIENT DIETS TO MICE

Diets cause varying degrees of distress or fitness, depending on which and how much of each food is present. The following materials fed to three or more mice should illustrate the point: (1) fifty per cent cornstarch plus fifty per cent sugar mixed with a small amount of bacon drippings, (2) whole-wheat bread, (3) whole-wheat bread, milk, and lettuce. Use recently weaned mice weighing about ten grams each for these experiments. Water the animals daily.

The mouse receiving cornstarch, sugar, and fat will obtain no vitamins, minerals, or proteins. The foods of this diet serve as fuel for heat and movement but will not maintain the muscles, blood, hair, and skeleton. This animal weakens and loses weight from the very beginning.

Whole-wheat bread, fed to the second mouse, is rich in the B complex, but low in vitamins A, C, and D, as well as calcium and phosphorus. The mouse manufactures some of the vitamin C in its own body, so watch for symptoms of vitamins A and D deficiencies. An inflamed area usually develops around the eyes, which remain closed much of the time. Growth and bone development are very slow.

Do not water the third mouse; give him milk instead. This can be prepared from powder if desired. Milk, bread, and a daily lettuce leaf give a relatively complete diet. Milk and lettuce are rich in vitamin A as well as other vitamins and minerals.

Record each day the weight, eye and skin condition, posture, and general vitality. Make graphs of the information on weight gain (Fig. 31–2). If you do not have a scale, a crude one may be made by attaching a hacksaw blade to a four-inch-high wooden support. Weigh mice in a small pan glued to the unattached end of the blade. Put graph paper on a board behind the pan. Calibrate your scale by adding nickels to the pan (a nickel weighs five grams) and making marks on the paper for one- and five-gram divisions.

Continue the starch, sugar, and fat diet for only one week, lest the experiment prove fatal. Continue the other diets for two weeks. At these times place all animals on the bread, milk, and lettuce diet, or on regular mouse chow. Note the rapid return of weight and health to those mice which were previously malnourished.

## OTHER THINGS TO DO

In this experiment you see dramatic changes, both physical and behavioral. There should remain no doubt about the favorable influence of vitamins on health. However, you may wish to pursue the subject, demonstrating deficiencies of other nutrients. The General Biological Supply House maintains a large stock of prepared diets for getting deficiencies of protein, fat, carbohydrate, minerals, and a variety of vitamins. These may be bought in either one-pound or three-pound

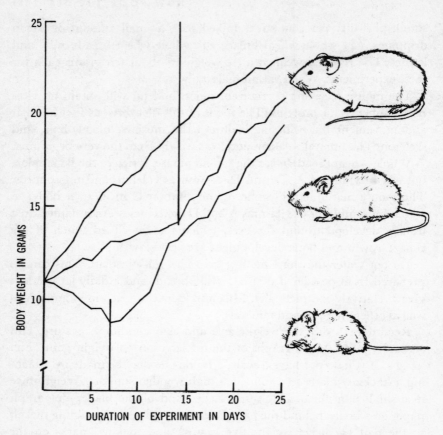

**Fig. 31–2 DIET EFFECTS ON GROWTH OF MICE**

The top mouse received a balanced diet of milk, bread, and lettuce. The middle mouse received bread only for fourteen days, then was changed to milk, bread, and lettuce. The lower mouse received starch, sugar, and fat for seven days, then was changed to milk, bread, and lettuce.

packages. They also supply Turtox Service Leaflet No. 49, "Nutrition Experiments," and a more detailed booklet, "Laboratory experiments in nutrition with special reference to the laboratory care of the white rat." Diets suitable for rats should work also with mice, except that the latter require a reduced quantity of feed.

For a factual account of progress in the food field, read the numerous short stories by O. E. Byrd, *Nutrition Sourcebook,* Stanford University Press, Stanford, California, 1955.

# The Heart and Circulation

## 32
## THE GREAT BLOOD PUMP

**Materials.**
1. Beef, sheep, or pig heart
2. Dissecting instruments

**Heart mending.** Completely shut off the blood supply to the brain and it is irreversibly damaged within three minutes. Should the heart stop pumping, or if some major blood vessel is blocked, death occurs in but a slightly longer time.

Until the early 1950s, major heart and vessel operations were rarely undertaken. The time margin of safety was too short and the risks too great. Animal experimentation, however, indicated that those with lowered body temperatures have a diminished heart rate and a diminished need for oxygen. Application of artificially induced low body temperatures to patients enabled surgeons to shut off the blood completely for periods up to thirty minutes.

Almost simultaneously, other researchers were experimenting with mechanical hearts and lungs. But exact duplication of the real organs is no easy task. The heart circulates two and one-half gallons of unclotted blood per minute. It pumps red blood cells through lung capillaries so small that the cells must move in single file. During each pulsation the fluid exposed to fresh air in the lungs equals the area of a badminton court. Technical difficulties in artificially oxygenating the blood rapidly, yet gently so as not to damage the cells, have been enormous.

Fortunately, heart-lung machines have been constructed and do work. During use, the real heart may be completely shut off, permitting operations in a dry, bloodless area. Blood returning through the superior and inferior venae cavae (Figs. 32–1 and 32–2) is shunted through a mechanical pump to a mechanical oxygenator and then back to the aorta where it passes normally through the rest of the body. Use of such devices has allowed surgical bypass of the heart for one hour and, with modification, for even longer durations.

There is one other advance which should be mentioned. Many years ago a medical investigator discovered that blood vessels from one animal could successfully be used to replace and repair those of another animal of the same species. This fact was eventually applied to man and artery banks became the vogue. Now researchers have found that woven plastic tubes such as those of nylon, dacron, and teflon can be substituted for the same purpose.

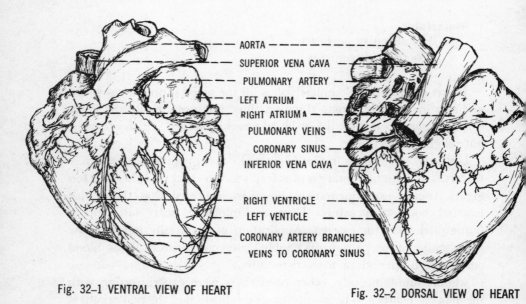

AORTA

SUPERIOR VENA CAVA

PULMONARY ARTERY

LEFT ATRIUM

RIGHT ATRIUM

PULMONARY VEINS

CORONARY SINUS

INFERIOR VENA CAVA

RIGHT VENTRICLE

LEFT VENTICLE

CORONARY ARTERY BRANCHES

VEINS TO CORONARY SINUS

Fig. 32–1 VENTRAL VIEW OF HEART          Fig. 32–2 DORSAL VIEW OF HEART

Heart mending is still a relatively new art. Former invalids, some with holes of the inside heart wall, some with narrow, stiffened, leaky valves, some with constricted vessels, now work and play normally.

## THE HEART ALSO NEEDS BLOOD

Strangely enough, blood within the atria and ventricles does not directly nourish the heart wall. Special vessels called coronaries carry oxygen and food to heart muscle. If these arteries are blocked, a condition develops called *coronary occlusion*. The heart is deprived of vital materials and can no longer pump effectively. Coronary occlusion is a leading killer of people in middle and old age.

Procure from a slaughterhouse a beef, sheep, or pig heart with major blood vessels attached. Examine the outside of this heart. Vessels are often surrounded by fatty tissue, making them more readily visible. *Coronary arteries* exit from the *aorta* and run across the ventral (chest wall) side of the heart (Fig. 32–1). Thinner-walled, darker-colored *coronary veins* run near the arteries and return blood into an enlarged *coronary sinus* on the back, or dorsal side of the heart (Fig. 32–2). The blood then drains back into the right atrium.

**The path through the heart.** Do not yet cut open the heart. Trace the course of blood through it (remaining outside to retain normal structural relations) by starting with the venae cavae (Figs. 32–1 and 32–2; see also Fig. 33–1). Blood returning from veins passes through the *superior* and *inferior venae cavae* and into the *right atrium* (sometimes called right auricle). Run a finger or probe down these two large vessels to prove this fact. From the right atrium blood is sucked into the *right ventricle* and then pumped through the *pulmonary artery* to both lungs. Carrying a fresh load of oxygen, it returns to the *left atrium* through four *pulmonary veins*. Passing from here to the *left ventricle* it presently is forced under tremendous pressure through the heavy walled aorta into arteries coursing throughout the body.

**Inside the heart.** Open the heart by slitting first the right atrium and right ventricle. The beauty and strength of the interwoven, reinforced fibrous architecture will catch your attention at once (Fig. 32–3). This greatly strengthens the heart. Notice the muscular walls, heavier in the ventricle. See the large *right atrioventricular valve* (abbreviated A-V valve). There are three flaps to this valve, part of which may have been destroyed in cutting. Pull the *tendinous cords* attached to the flaps. These are operated by contraction of *papillary muscles,* special extensions of the heart wall. When open, the valve admits blood from the atrium. Notice also where blood enters the atrium from the venae cavae and its exit from the right ventricle through the pulmonary artery. Three half-moon shaped valves are present at the beginning of this artery to prevent a back flow of blood to the heart once it has been expelled. These are called *semilunar* valves.

Slit open the left atrium and left ventricle. The structure is similar to the right side except for the extremely thick wall of the left ventricle. This is necessary since this chamber must pump blood to the entire body

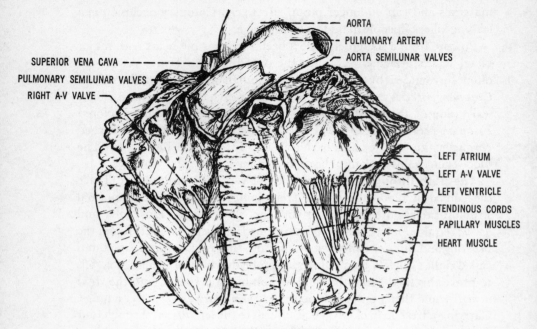

AORTA
PULMONARY ARTERY
AORTA SEMILUNAR VALVES
SUPERIOR VENA CAVA
PULMONARY SEMILUNAR VALVES
RIGHT A-V VALVE
LEFT ATRIUM
LEFT A-V VALVE
LEFT VENTRICLE
TENDINOUS CORDS
PAPILLARY MUSCLES
HEART MUSCLE

Fig. 32–3 INSIDE A BEEF HEART

(except the lungs), including the most distant parts of the head, hands, and feet. Find the pulmonary veins at their entrance to the left atrium. Locate also the left A-V valve (only two flaps on this side), tendinous cords, and papillary muscles, and the exit of blood through the aorta with its three semilunar valves.

## OTHER THINGS TO DO

If you have not already examined the fish heart (Chapter 11), now is the time to do it. Compare its two chambers with the three chambers of amphibian and reptile hearts and the four chambers of mammals and birds. The latter is the most efficient system for distributing "used" blood to the lungs and freshly oxygenated blood to the body.

Invertebrates, too, often have circulatory systems. As an example, you may look at a clam's heart. Using a knife blade, pry open the animal's shell and cut the muscles at each end, the ones which hold the shell shut. Open wide to totally expose the body within. At one side of the hinge, sometimes slightly buried under other tissues, is a slowly-beating, watery bag—the heart. The circulatory fluid is colorless and transparent, not red and opaque as in vertebrates. Warm the shell and watch the heart speed up. Cool it, and the beat slows or stops altogether.

Blood vessels in more remote regions may also be traced. Dealers often inject the vessels of their preserved specimens with colored latex rubber, a valuable aid to the beginner. Arteries are red, veins are blue. For a little more money you get animals with dyed lymphatics, a special normally hard-to-see system of vessels discussed in the following chapter.

# 33

# THE MOTION OF BLOOD CELLS

**Materials.**
1. Frog
2. Microscope
3. Ether and cotton
4. Cardboard
5. Straight pins

**Transporting oxygen and carbon dioxide.** Foods are "burned" in the presence of oxygen to give energy for activity. We recognize in this a retarded resemblance to the quick-burning blaze of a candle, which also consumes air's vital gas. And just as a candle flickers out in a closed container, so also is man's "fire" extinguished without oxygen.

*Red blood cells* are the all important deliverers of oxygen, carrying it just as cars of a train carry freight. The pickup depot is in the lungs; receiving depots are in the head, hands, feet, stomach, and all other parts of the body (Fig. 33–1). As oxygen is unloaded, the waste gas, carbon dioxide, jumps aboard for the return trip to the lungs where it is breathed off. The *plasma,* or liquid portion of the blood is also significant for these transfers. Some oxygen and much carbon dioxide are transported in the plasma.

**Infection and the white blood cells.** There are almost 1000 times as many red blood cells as there are white blood cells in the circulatory system, but there is only one type of red cell. The white cells are of several types, namely: (1) neutrophils, (2) basophils, (3) eosinophils, (4) monocytes, and (5) lymphocytes. Neutrophils comprise about two thirds of the white-cell count in man. The remaining cells are mostly lymphocytes plus a small percentage of each of the other types.

White blood cells are essential for the control of infection within the body. Two of the most notably active cells in this respect are the *neutrophils* and *monocytes.* These cells move about in the blood stream

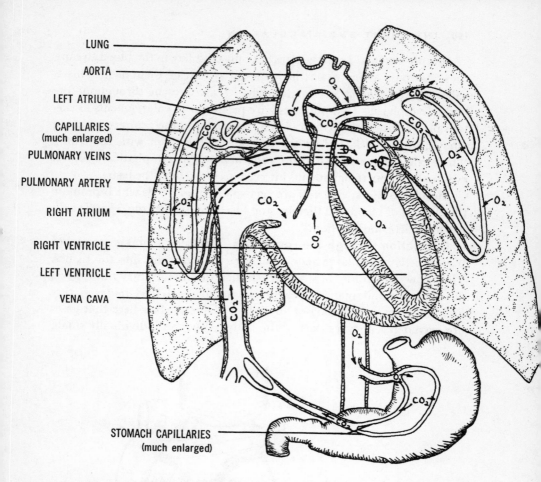

LUNG
AORTA
LEFT ATRIUM
CAPILLARIES
(much enlarged)
PULMONARY VEINS
PULMONARY ARTERY
RIGHT ATRIUM
RIGHT VENTRICLE
LEFT VENTRICLE
VENA CAVA

STOMACH CAPILLARIES
(much enlarged)

Fig. 33–1 THE EXCHANGE OF RESPIRATORY GASES IN THE LUNGS AND BODY TISSUES

under their own power. When foreign substances (bacteria) enter the blood, as through a cut toe, these travel to the source of infection to engulf and digest the foreign particles.

Acute infections such as tonsillitis and appendicitis are usually checked by the neutrophils. Chronic conditions such as tuberculosis (t.b.) are controlled primarily by *lymphocytes*. Lymphocytes produce substances which bring about *immunity* to certain diseases. An example of an immune condition is the resistance to polio conferred by the Salk vaccine. The importance of basophils and eosinophils is uncertain at the present time.

**Lymph vessels.** Lymphocytes not only circulate in the blood stream, they also pass along vessels in a special system of their own. This is called the *lymphatic system*. Lymphatics are present throughout the body. Lymph cells (lymphocytes) are produced in enlargements at certain places within the lymph vessels, especially in the armpits, near the elbows, in the neck, and at the junction of the thigh with the trunk. These enlargements are called *lymph nodes*. The lymphatic vessels all eventually empty their contents into venous blood near the heart.

**Blood platelets.** *Platelets* are very small, fragile cells which promote the clotting of blood and thereby stop bleeding. In the frog, *spindle cells* perform this same function.

**Circulation through the capillaries.** The body's vital gases do not pass directly out of large vessels, the arteries and veins, into the tissues. They flow only inside these. To reach their destination they must travel along smaller and smaller tubes till they finally reach the *capillaries,* tiny invisible pipes only 0.0007 of an inch in diameter. It is here that gases are exchanged in every part of the body. Although individually small,

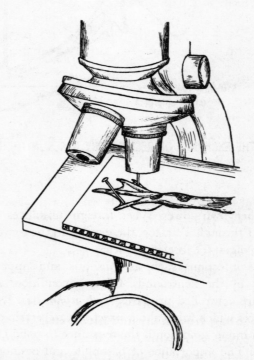

Fig. 33–2 SEEING THE CIRCULATION IN A FROG'S WEB

capillaries are so numerous that their total length in one human is almost 60,000 miles, and their total bulk is over twice that of the liver.

Not all capillaries open at the same time. If this does happen, as in shock, the patient fades more and more as increasing numbers of capillaries expand. Eventually he perishes as blood stagnates in the tissues, becoming unavailable for the heart to pump. Normally, circular muscle cells present at the entrances to capillaries allow only a trickle of blood to pass through, and sometimes they completely shut off, reopening during exercise or at other times when blood is needed.

What controls the normal contraction and expansion of capillaries? At present there is some doubt, but many suitable suggestions. Probably epinephrine and ACH, chemicals derived from the autonomic nervous system, are of some importance. Experimentally, even very dilute solutions of epinephrine cause constriction and ACH brings about enlargement. In addition, metabolic tissue wastes, abundant during exercise, depress and relax capillary muscles. This permits more blood flow at a time when it is most needed. Hormones from the adrenal cortex also significantly maintain tone of the circulatory system.

## HOW TO SEE CIRCULATING BLOOD IN A FROG FOOT

Secure a piece of corrugated cardboard large enough to support the entire body of a frog. At one end of this piece cut out a circular opening about one-half inch in diameter. Anesthetize a frog by placing it in a small closed container with ether. As soon as he stops struggling, remove him to the piece of cardboard. Keep a wad of cotton dampened with ether on the frog's body to prevent a return to consciousness. Put the web of one hind foot over the hole in the cardboard. Pin it in place with two or three straight pins (Fig. 33–2). Put the cardboard and frog on the stage of a microscope. Use low power and adjust the reflecting mirror so that light shines maximally through the web. Do you see pulses of blood? The pulses are most apparent in relatively large vessels called *arterioles* (Fig. 33–3). Arterioles receive blood from arteries and pass it on to capillaries. Watch the small round discs traveling single file through tiny capillaries. These are red blood cells and an occasional white blood cell. They go next into *venules* and then to veins. Count the pulsations. How does this compare with the heart rate?

**The beating frog heart and blood cells.** If you have not yet witnessed the throb of a living heart, this is the time to do it. Cut open the chest wall and observe the heart (Fig. 29–1). The single ventricle has a thick muscular wall which is lightly colored. The two atria are darker

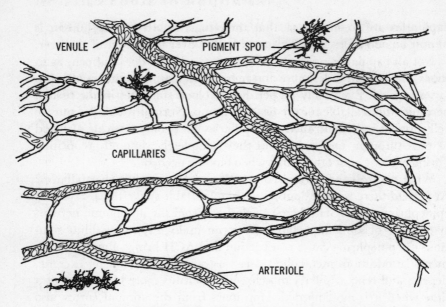

VENULE  PIGMENT SPOT

CAPILLARIES

ARTERIOLE

Fig. 33–3 MAGNIFIED BLOOD VESSELS IN A FROG'S WEB

and somewhat buried beneath the head end of the ventricle. Watch the beat. Note that both atria contract at the same time. This is followed shortly by ventricular contraction.

Cut the heart from the frog. It will die painlessly without recovering from ether anesthesia. Squeeze a small amount of blood from the heart onto a microscope slide. Dilute this with a drop of frog saline solution (0.7 gm. salt in 100 ml. water). Cover the sample with a cover slip and observe with both low and high power of the microscope.

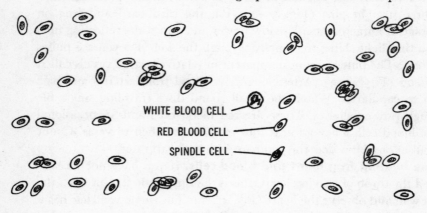

WHITE BLOOD CELL

RED BLOOD CELL

SPINDLE CELL

Fig. 33–4 BLOOD CELLS OF THE FROG

Red blood cells compose the vast majority of observed cells. These have a pale yellow or red color and usually contain a darkened nucleus in the center (Fig. 33–4). White blood cells and spindle cells may be seen, but infrequently so. These have irregular shapes and almost no color. Their nuclei are slightly darkened masses at the center of the cells. Spindle cells are more elongated than are the white blood cells.

## OTHER THINGS TO DO

You may want to alter the circulation in your frog's web before removing its heart. Drip ice water on his foot to reduce the blood flow, then add warm water to increase it. Add a drop of commercial epinephrine. This sometimes causes complete closure of certain capillaries.

Other animals may be used in place of frogs. For instance, the thin, transparent tissue connecting the intestinal loops in a mouse shows a wealth of small vessels. Goldfish or minnow tails are also good. Wrap the fish in soaking wet cotton and hold his tail down with a glass plate or slide. Do not keep him from his aquarium for too long a period of time.

As reading material, you may desire the authoritative article by B. W. Zweifach, "The microcirculation of the blood," *Scientific American,* 200:54, January 1959. In addition, read the book by B. Cabot, *The Motion of the Heart,* Harper and Brothers, New York, 1954. Written to acquaint laymen with the many facets of circulatory research, this book does the job in a most magnificent manner.

# 34

# HEMOGLOBIN—THE RED PIGMENT

**Materials.**
1. Hemolets or sterilized needle
2. Rubbing alcohol
3. Mouse, ether, cotton, beaker, and scissors
4. Tallqvist standard hemoglobin scale

**Blood and acclimatization.** On May 29, 1953, Sir Edmund Hillary and his colleague, Tensing Norkay, stood at Mount Everest's summit and patted each other on the back. No one had been there before; perhaps no one would come again. Oxygen pressure at this altitude, 29,000 feet, is less than one third that at sea level. The Everest expedition depended heavily on supplies of this gas which they carried. But Hillary took off his mask at the peak for ten minutes. That he could do this and survive points out the exceptional adaptability of the human body.

Serious climbers allow several weeks of acclimation to the mountains before they make their most difficult ascents. First attempts at exertion leave them tired and breathless, but in time they make numerous stamina-building adjustments. One of these is respiratory—more air is inhaled with each breath. Of equal or greater importance are changes in the circulatory system: (1) the heart pumps more blood (temporarily, except at the highest altitudes), (2) the number of red blood cells rise, and (3) the blood assumes a deeper color which indicates an increase in its pigment, hemoglobin (Fig. 34–1). Each of these changes helps the body achieve its normal oxygen requirement despite the rarity of the air.

There are practical limits to these means of acclimation. On earth the highest permanent settlement is in the Andes at 17,500 feet. The men who live here work daily in a mine at 19,000 feet. Scientists of the Everest expedition believe this is the top altitude at which humans can

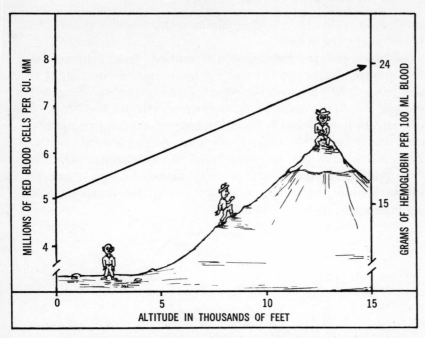

Fig. 34–1 RED BLOOD CELLS AND HEMOGLOBIN RELATED TO ALTITUDE

persistently acclimate, although temporary improvement is noticed up to 23,000 feet. Above this height there is steady deterioration. Hillary and Tensing were unable to remain more than a few days near Everest's peak.

**Hemoglobin, the key in the lock.** The red blood cells are doorways through which oxygen must enter the body's household. But without hemoglobin the doors are locked. *Hemoglobin* is the red-colored key which fits and is an integral part of each red blood cell. It is the part which actually receives and dispenses *oxygen*.

In the lungs twenty volumes of oxygen combine with every 100 volumes of blood. At rest, only twenty-five per cent of this load is lost to the tissues. But at high altitudes, during exercise, or in other air-deficient states, a much higher proportion is removed.

Hemoglobin has two more functions. One of these is the *transportation* of *carbon dioxide*. It returns some of the content to the lungs, although most goes in chemical combination with the blood's sodium and potassium. Hemoglobin also serves as a buffer, that is, it prevents excessive alterations in the blood's acid and base content. The body is very sensitive to changes in acid equilibrium. Death would quickly ensue if it were not for the buffers.

**Red blood cell and hemoglobin formation.** Iron, vitamin $B_{12}$, and a stomach factor are essential for the normal production of red blood cells and hemoglobin (Fig. 34–2). *Iron* is part of the hemoglobin molecule; in fact, it is the very part to which oxygen attaches. We get the iron from our foods, *Vitamin $B_{12}$*, also taken with the diet, stimulates the production of blood cells by the spongy inner portion of bone called the *marrow*. The backbones, breastbone, and ribs are the most significant in this respect. But the vitamin must be absorbed before it can act, and this is brought about by a substance with the simple-sounding, descriptive name, *stomach factor*.

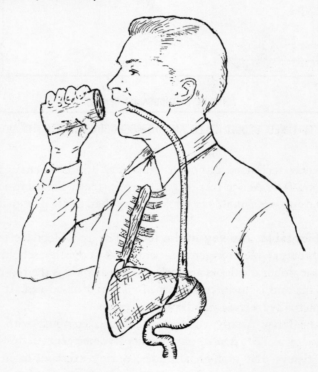

**Fig. 34–2 CONTROL OF RBC AND HEMOGLOBIN PRODUCTION**
Iron and vitamin $B_{12}$, taken with the diet, are absorbed through the gastrointestinal tract and stored in the liver. When released, the vitamin stimulates the production of red blood cells in bone marrow; iron becomes part of the oxygen-carrying hemoglobin of blood cells.

Normally there are about fifteen grams of hemoglobin in every 100 milliliters of blood (abbreviated 15 gm.%). There are conditions called *anemias* in which hemoglobin may decrease to five grams per cent or less. Similar or even greater reductions of red blood cells may occur. The most serious of these takes place in the disease of *pernicious anemia,* which gets its name from the Latin word *pernicies,* meaning "ruin." In pernicious anemia the red blood cell count may drop to ten per cent of its normal value. Until 1926 the disease was fatal and untreatable. Experiments a few years earlier had shown that meals of liver fed to partially bled dogs brought prompt recovery of cell counts. When lightly cooked liver was eaten by human anemia patients, including those with pernicious anemia, they also obtained relief, and dramatically so! We now know that vitamin $B_{12}$ is stored in the liver and that the vitamin as well as the organ can bring life to patients who would formerly have died.

## HOW TO GET BLOOD FROM THE HUMAN FINGER

Blood can be obtained simply by puncturing the skin with a previously unused dissecting needle or with a small sharp blade. Sterilize these with heat (boiling water for thirty minutes) and cleanse the end of the finger with alcohol. Allow the alcohol to dry before making a small cut.

More convenient are the small, razor-sharp *Hemolets* available from the Aloe Scientific Company. Each blade comes in a separate, sterilized package ready for use. A quick, short thrust is all that is needed to get one or two drops of blood. Hemolets are inexpensively sold in lots of 250, a suitable size for schools but not for individuals.

**How to get blood from a mouse tail.** Place the mouse in an inverted beaker which contains cotton soaked in ether. As soon as the animal is unconscious, remove it from the beaker. Snip off about one-half inch of the tail. One or more drops of blood will appear at the cut end, ready for a hemoglobin determination. Return the mouse to its cage. Clotting will prevent further loss of blood by hemorrhage.

**Hemoglobin determination by a color scale.** Obtain a Tallqvist hemoglobin color scale (Fig. 34–3). This scale will show red colors of varying intensity. The deeper the red the more hemoglobin is present. The paler or more yellow-tinted the color, the less hemoglobin is present. Small circular holes appear in the center of each of the colored portions.

Use clean white filter paper for absorbing blood from the punctured

STANDARD HEMOGLOBIN SCALE
Grams of Hemoglobin in 100 ML of Blood

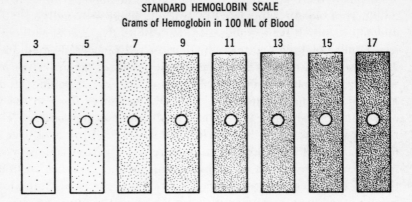

Fig. 34–3 SCALE FOR DETERMINING HEMOGLOBIN

finger or clipped tail. Place two drops of blood on this paper, spacing them the same distance apart as the holes on the color scale. Allow the drops to be absorbed into the paper. As soon as the glossy appearance of the blood has disappeared, compare the unknown sample with the scale. Do this by moving the filter paper back and forth between the circular holes until a color match is obtained. Express this value as grams of hemoglobin in 100 cubic centimeters of blood.

Although Tallqvist scales give reasonable estimates, their accuracy should not be confused with more reliable methods used in research. Many of these call for an analysis of the blood's iron, since there is a definite ratio of this in hemoglobin. Others require photoelectric measurements of the color of blood.

## OTHER THINGS TO DO

Frequently the experimenter wants both the hemoglobin content and the red blood cell count. These do not always parallel each other, although ideally they should. The device for measuring cell counts, the *hemocytometer*, is sold by many of the suppliers listed in the appendix. Directions accompany each instrument, but basically the idea is to draw blood from the finger, dilute it, and count either red or white cells on a scaled slide under the miscroscope.

If you can obtain a microscope with the high-power, so-called oil immersion lens, you may want to look at blood smears. These are made by putting a drop of blood at one end of a clean slide, then bringing a second slide, held at a thirty-degree angle, in contact with the drop (Fig. 34–4). Now push the second slide continually across the first to form a uniformly thin smear. Let this dry. Pour on a small quantity of Wright's stain for one minute, then an equal quantity of buffer solution for four minutes (both fluids are available from dealers). Wash off the buffer and air dry the slide. Under the microscope you will recognize numerous disc-shaped red cells plus infrequent purple-stained white cells of many different types.

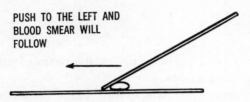

PUSH TO THE LEFT AND
BLOOD SMEAR WILL
FOLLOW

Fig. 34–4 MAKING A BLOOD SMEAR

# 35

# CONTROL OF THE HEART

**Materials.**
1. Turtle
2. Ether, saw or ax, pliers, ice pick, and dissecting instruments
3. Sodium chloride (table salt)
4. Batteries and electric wire, inductorium if available
5. Test tubes for hot and iced water
6. String or heavy thread, and watch with second hand

**Excitation of the heart.** Those who look at living embryos see hearts throbbing at a very early stage of development. In fact, they start even before nerves reach them. There is only one conclusion to be drawn. The heart can operate without the brain's help. A basic rhythm is always present; the nerves merely alter the rate. To demonstrate this axiom you need no embryos. The next time you catch fish, or after experimenting with a turtle, remove the heart and drop it in saline solution. It may beat for minutes, or it may beat for days. In any event you prove the point.

Biologists who inspect warm-blooded hearts cut away from the body find the ventricles are first to cease beating, next the left atrium, then the right atrium. If they now make a careful examination, they see a slight quiver near the junction of the atria and large entering veins, even though the atrium itself does not function. This quiver shows the location of the heart's pacemaker, the part which originates the beat. In mammals and birds it goes by the name *sinoatrial,* or *S-A node.* The pacemaker for fish, amphibians, and reptiles is called the *sinus venosus.* This is a blood-filled chamber, not just a node of tissue. But it is found at the same location, at the heart's entrance.

Conductile fibers from the S-A node (or sinus venosus) transfer the rhythmic beat across the heart (Fig. 35-1). First, impulses travel rapidly across the atria, causing atrial contraction. In approaching the ventricles, they are delayed at a second node called the *atrioventricular,* or *A-V node.* Speeding up again, they travel through the ventricles, causing simultaneous contraction. The delay at the A-V node causes separate beating of atria and ventricles, giving the normal two-beat, or lub-dup sound.

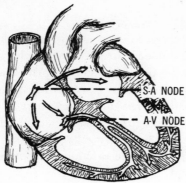

Fig. 35–1 HUMAN HEART CONDUCTILE SYSTEM

**Heart block, and heart disease.** Lub-lub dup, lub-lub dup . . . this is the sound of an inefficient heart, a heart with its conductile system partially blocked. If some disease of mechanical blockage prevents impulses from passing into the ventricles, they will set up a rhythm slower than that of the pacemaking S-A node. There will result two or more beats of the atria for every single beat of the ventricles.

Complete blocking of all impulses from the S-A node allows the ventricles to assume a slow beat which has no relation to the atrial beat. Blood is very poorly pumped from such a heart.

The various abnormalities of conduction are readily diagnosed with a machine called the *electrocardiograph.* The heart produces minute electrical impulses with each discharge of the S-A node into the heart muscles. By amplifying the impulses, they can be traced out on paper. A study of such tracings is imperative for the physician who studies heart disease.

**Nerve control of the beat.** During exercise or emotional bouts the heart pace accelerates considerably. This is controlled primarily by impulses traveling along autonomic nerves to the S-A and A-V nodes. The nerves (ten in man) which increase heart rate are called sympathetic nerves. The hormone epinephrine, which is released from these nerves at the heart wall, speeds the heart.

Slowing of the heart is controlled by vagus parasympathetic nerves. They release their hormone, acetylcholine. There are two vagus nerves. The right one goes to the S-A node, the left to the A-V node. By electrically stimulating the vagus, one can produce sufficient impulses to slow or even stop the heart.

## DISPLAYING THE TURTLE HEART

First the animal must be given ether and/or pithed to relieve it of all sensation. Allow one-half to one hour for a turtle to become unconscious from ether. Pithing is accomplished by grasping the head and pulling it out with pliers or by a hook on the upper jaw. Next, stick an ice pick into the brain and destroy it. Do this by insertion at the back of the head, forcing the point forward beneath the skull bone (Fig. 35–2). Thorough destruction of the brain prevents pain. Now run the ice pick down the spinal cord. This completes the double pithing. The animal is ready for the experiment.

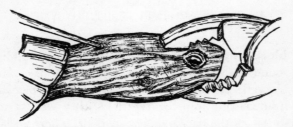

PUSH PICK FORWARD INTO BRAIN, THEN
BACKWARD INTO SPINAL CORD

**Fig. 35–2 PITHING A TURTLE**

To find the heart, the lower shell (*plastron*) must be removed. Do this by sawing at the two junctions of the plastron with the upper shell (or chop with ax). When the shells are separated, run a knife blade along the plastron underside, staying as close as possible to the plastron. Remove this bottom shell. The beating heart is now exposed, but is beneath a transparent layer of tissue called the *pericardium*. Remove this also.

Watch the two atria contract, followed by contraction of the single ventricle (Fig. 35–3). Count the number of beats per minute. Sprinkle the heart occasionally with saline solution (0.7 gm. sodium chloride/ 100 ml. water) to prevent drying.

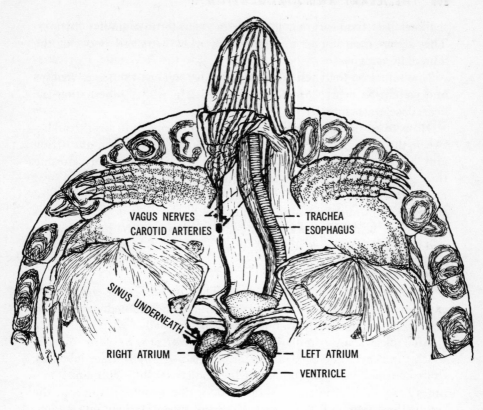

**VAGUS NERVES**
**CAROTID ARTERIES**

**TRACHEA**
**ESOPHAGUS**

**SINUS UNDERNEATH**

**RIGHT ATRIUM**

**LEFT ATRIUM**

**VENTRICLE**

Fig. 35–3 HEART AND VAGUS NERVES OF TURTLE DISSECTION

**Locating and stimulating the vagus nerves.** These nerves are found by looking deep within the neck (Fig. 35–3). Pull the turtle's head outward with pliers. Locate the trachea and beneath this the esophagus. When the nerves are found, gently tease them apart from surrounding connective tissue, and stimulate with a weak electric current from an *inductorium* (an instrument which generates and administers induction shocks) or by repeated rapid contacts by wires from two poles of a battery. If the heart slows, you have the vagus. Stimulate with a stronger current and the heart stops completely but beats again upon removal of the stimulation.

**The effects of heat and cold.** The sinus venosus is the enlargement where the veins enter the right atrium (Fig. 35–3). Warm a beaker of water to about 40°C. Fill a small test tube with the water and immediately place it against the sinus venosus. The heart speeds up. Time the beat. In warm weather the heart accelerates in a similar manner. This allows more blood to circulate to meet increased needs of the animal for activity.

Now place a small test tube of ice water against the sinus venosus and watch the heart slow. Count the beat. In winter hibernation the heart decelerates similarly.

**How to get heart block.**   Loop a piece of string or heavy thread between the atria and ventricle. Make a single loose tie in the string and gradually tighten it. The tie prevents impulses from crossing through conductile fibers to the ventricle. The atria continue to beat at a normal rate, while the ventricles will beat at one half or one third this rate. Continue tightening. Eventually the ventricle stops or assumes a very slow beat independent of the atria. What are the rates of atrial and ventricular contraction now?

## OTHER THINGS TO DO

Turtle hearts are unusually strong. They make perfect subjects for experiments such as this. However, if turtles are not immediately available, frogs may be substituted. Bullfrogs work especially well.

After electrically stimulating the vagus, you may want to directly shock the heart. These extra stimuli, applied at appropriate intervals, cause contractions which do not fit the regular rhythm. Humans sometimes have similar premature contractions due to minor upsets in the conductile system. These are more frequent during fatigue, but seldom are indicative of poor health.

After completing the turtle experiment, you may want to remove the heart and put it in saline, as suggested earlier in this chapter. Find out how long it takes to stop beating and observe what parts are first to go. If oxygen is bubbled through the water or if glucose plus a small amount of calcium and potassium are added, the heart will function for an even longer period of time.

# 36
# THE PULSATING HEART

**Materials.**
1. Stethoscope (optional, can be homemade)
2. A metronome or pendulum clock
3. A 20-inch-high step or chair

**Heart governors.** Lub-dup, LUB-DUP, LUB-DUP—these are the sounds of the heart as a man starts to run. Louder and louder, faster and faster goes the beat. The heart pumps powerfully as it pounds the chest wall. The arteries bulge and the blood pressure rockets. What brings about this ever-ready response?

First, even when a man anticipates exercise, as before the starter's gun, his body prepares. The thought of activity signals the *cardioaccelerator center* in the brain's *medulla*. This center connects with sympathetic nerves to the heart, the ones which augment its rate and output. Anyone who doubts the mind's influence on heart rate should consider records of a Navy balloon ascension in 1956. The balloon drifted into a hazardous thunderstorm. Telemetered data on the confined, relatively inactive crew revealed heart rates that were never less than 160 beats per minute! Compare this with the normal rate of seventy to eighty beats per minute.

The actual start of exercise forces an immediate output increase via the same accelerator mechanism. But there are other factors now. The blood flows through under heavy pressure, and the pumping action of muscles adds its force to the flow. Nerve receptors at the heart's entrance respond to the pressure by further exciting the medulla's accelerator. Pressure also stretches the heart's muscle fibers and, like rubber bands, they contract with reinforced vigor. This increases the ejection of blood and prevents overexpansion of the heart chambers.

There is another means of altering the cardiac response. In the walls of the carotid arteries and aortic arch are structures sensitive to chemical changes, called *chemoreceptors* (Fig. 36–1). These control respiration primarily, but they also govern the heart. During exhaustive activity, when blood oxygen is deficient and carbon dioxide excessive, the heart quickens via a nerve reflex from these receptors.

And lest the blood pressure rise high enough to endanger the more fragile blood vessels, the circulatory system has its variation of safety gauges and valves. The "gauges," called *pressoreceptors,* are sensitive nerve endings in the carotids and aorta. High pressures expand these vessels and by reflex inhibit the heart. This reduces the blood pressure to tolerable limits. On the other hand, if the pressure becomes too low, these receptors relay messages which hurry the beat.

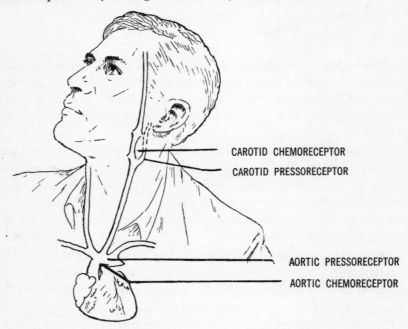

CAROTID CHEMORECEPTOR
CAROTID PRESSORECEPTOR

AORTIC PRESSORECEPTOR
AORTIC CHEMORECEPTOR

Fig. 36–1 RECEPTORS OF THE CAROTID ARTERIES AND AORTIC ARCH

**Exercise and athletes.** Fred Wilt was an Olympic two-miler whose resting heart and pulse rate stood in the fifties. At Purdue, we compared his recovery with that of two normally inactive graduate students. In a half-mile, three-minute run, a pace which thoroughly exhausted the students, Wilt was no more fatigued than the ordinary man after a morning stroll. After two minutes his heart rate was seventy-two and in twenty minutes he had completely recovered. The students had pulses over 120 after the same two minutes and were over 100 when Wilt was normal.

If we stay physically fit, our bodies respond easily to exertion. Exercise strengthens heart muscle just as it strengthens skeletal muscle. For this reason, an athlete's heart can pump more blood during each contraction. This enables the same quantity of blood to be circulated at a slower rate (notice that Wilt's pulse was in the fifties). A forceful beat also promotes rapid recovery.

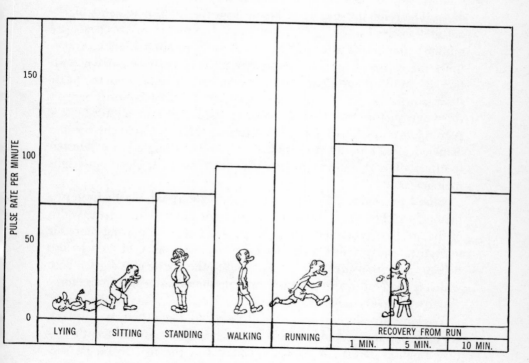

Fig. 36–2 POSITION AND EXERCISE EFFECTS ON PULSE

**Standing versus sitting (Fig. 36–2).** While standing at attention, soldiers often remain immobile for long periods of time. Gravity drains blood from the head to the legs. Unless they stir up the circulation by wiggling their toes and contracting calf muscles, they topple in a faint. This reaction happens more frequently on warm days when vessels are relaxed, so that blood stagnates even faster.

As we have learned, pressoreceptors respond to blood reduction by increasing the heart rate. If the pulse is recorded while sitting and compared with that while standing, there will likely be a difference of five to ten beats per minute. While lying down, the rate is even slower. Those persons who are exceptionally fit will show only slight changes of heart rate or none at all. Their blood vessels, not their hearts, compensate for gravitational effects. Vessel tone raises the pressure and prevents a decrease in blood to the brain. Older people or those in poor condition sometimes feel faint upon standing. This is a consequence of relaxed vessels and slow circulation.

Pilots sometimes receive multiple gravity forces as they pull out of dives. The resultant sucking of blood from the brain may cause blackout and always causes a rise of heart rate (up to 150 or 200 beats per minute), the body's attempt to re-establish normal circulation. Sometimes the reverse happens; the aviator turns in an upside-down position. Blood fills the head and he "reds out." At the same time the heart slows down, courtesy of the pressoreceptors. In the laboratory we get the same picture by inverting subjects while tied to a "tilt-table." Astronauts and rocket pilots lie in reclining chairs to avoid the pooling of blood in extremities. In a horizontal position they can tolerate ten to fifteen times the normal gravity. At such times their blood outweighs molten lead.

**Blood pressure.** The pressure of your blood results mostly from two factors: (1) how much blood pours from the heart, and (2) the width of the arteries. When more blood is pumped, it's like putting more air in a tire; the pressure rises. Reducing the diameter of vessels also heightens the pressure. This is analogous to the nozzle of a garden hose which is partly turned shut. Such a nozzle spurts water with more force and to a greater distance.

We have not always known how to measure blood pressure; in fact, we have not always known there was such a thing. An eighteenth-century English clergyman, Stephen Hales, was the first to tangle successfully with this problem. He reasoned that since blood circulates (a fact discovered only 100 years earlier), it must be under pressure. To prove his point he tied a mare to a heavy field gate laid on the ground, then inserted a long tube into one of the arteries. The blood shot to a height of over nine feet, a gratifying experience for this investigator.

We humans might object if physicians used Reverend Hales's method, and besides it is too time-consuming. But researchers were slow to discover the simple apparatus which presently measures blood pressure; in fact, its basic parts were unknown till the late 1800s. The gadget to which we refer is the inflatable cuff and mercury tube common to any doctor's office. Pressure in the cuff shuts off an arm artery and simultaneously raises the mercury to a recordable height.

## LISTENING TO THE HEARTBEAT

Physicians in the old days placed their hands or ears on a patient's chest and felt or heard the familiar thump-thump. But in 1816 a French doctor named Laennec was confronted with an embarrassing situation. He was unable to feel the heartbeat of a young female patient excessively padded with fat and clothing. Rather than use his ear directly, he decided to roll paper into a cylinder and listen through this. It worked, and from this meager beginning, our present-day *stethoscopes* evolved.

You may purchase or make a workable stethoscope similar to your doctor's. Get a funnel, a Y-tube, and one short plus two long pieces of rubber tube. Connect the funnel and Y-tube, then run the long rubber tubes to the ears. Listen as shown in Fig. 36–3. Do you hear the double

Fig. 36–3 LISTENING TO THE HEART WITH A STETHOSCOPE

sound, a dull "lub-dup"? The "lub" is the sound of atrial contraction, and the "dup" represents the finished ventricular contraction.

**Feeling the pulse.** The pulse of blood flowing from the ventricles can be detected in several locations on the body. Among these are the carotid arteries of the neck and temporal arteries at the side of the head. The most common locale, however, is at the *radial artery* of the wrist (Fig. 36–4). To detect this pulse, place the thumb on the back side and the fingers over the radial artery on the underside of the wrist. The tester should exert only a medium pressure with his fingers to feel this pulse. Count the rate of artery expansions per minute. Note that this corresponds to the heart rate.

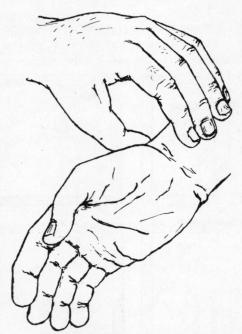

Fig. 36–4 TAKING THE PULSE

**Position and pulse.** Determine heart rates and pulses of subjects who are reclining, sitting, and standing. Keep the subjects quiet during such an examination. They should not have been engaged recently in work or play. Note that slight increases usually occur as they assume a more upright position.

**Step up for a step test.** Any type of strenuous exercise will be suitable for this experiment. Running in place or on the track, bicycle riding, and gymnastics readily encourage changes in heart rate. A more standardized procedure involves use of a "step" test. This test is commonly employed to determine physical fitness. At the same time it demonstrates the important changes in heart rate which occur with activity and recovery.

For this procedure a step or stool twenty inches in height is used. If such is not available, shorter stools or chairs may be used to illustrate the principle, although the physical-fitness index (described below) will not be valid. The subject should wear a minimum of clothing; gym clothes and rubber-soled shoes are satisfactory attire.

The observer must use a stop watch or watch with a second hand for timing. The subject steps up and down on the twenty-inch step. The observer must time the duration of his efforts and also call out the

Fig. 36–5 THE STEP TEST

proper stepping rhythm. A metronome or pendulum clock helps in this regard. Four stepping positions are used (Fig. 36–5). Each step is made at half-second intervals. The observer calls the changes of steps as—up, two, three, four; up, two, three, four, etc. The signal "up" should be made at exactly two-second intervals.

Now you should be ready for the actual test. Have the subject stand directly in front, facing the twenty-inch step. At the signal "up," he places his right foot on the platform; (2) he draws up his left foot and stands erect on the chair; (3) he lowers his left foot to the floor; and at (4) he brings down his right foot. The subject is now in the starting position again. He continues stepping as the observer calls changes in position.

Exercise the subject for five minutes or until he quits from exhaustion or until he can no longer maintain the stepping pace for a period of twenty seconds. When finished, have him sit down. Record the duration of exercise and start taking his pulse at once. This first pulse measurement is for your own information, not part of the physical-fitness index described in the next paragraph.

Record the heart rate or pulse again at one minute, two minutes, and three minutes, following the exercise test. Count the pulse for only thirty seconds during each measurement. Plug these counts into the following formula to get the subject's score:

$$\text{Index} = \frac{\text{duration of exercise in seconds} \times 100}{2 \times \text{the sum of the 30-second pulse counts}}$$

A score below fifty is considered poor. Fifty to eighty is average. An index above eighty is indicative of good physical fitness.

Continue recording every five minutes for a half hour or so. How rapid is the subject's recovery?

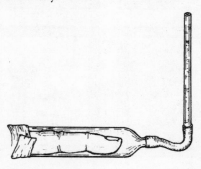

Fig. 36–6 FINGER PLETHYSMOGRAPH

## OTHER THINGS TO DO

There is a device which encloses a finger or hand and which goes by the name *plethysmograph*. This curious apparatus measures the blood volume of the part which it surrounds. As you may well imagine, blood volume changes each time the pulse rushes into the hand. When filled with water, a plethysmograph faithfully records each pulse, and if the water column is attached to an air-filled rubber diaphragm (a tambour), this vibrates, and a lever on top is moved up and down. Reasonably inexpensive finger plethysmographs may be bought from dealers in physiological apparatus or made by heating large-diameter polyethylene or glass tubing and pulling it into the shape shown in Fig. 36–6. One-inch width adhesive tape can be used to close off the junction of the tube with the finger. With these you may demonstrate changes in blood volume due to loud noises, ice cubes on the neck, excitement, and so forth.

For reading material we suggest the understandable exercise treatise by S. R. Riedman, *The Physiology of Work and Play,* The Dryden Press, Inc., New York, 1950.

# 37
# WHAT TYPE AM I?

**Materials.**
1. Anti-A and Anti-B serums
2. Sterile needle or blades such as Hemolets
3. Microscope (optional, but desired)
4. Microscope slide
5. Toothpicks

**Transfusion in the old days.** The lamb is a docile creature who would certainly harm no man, and yet there were many who suffered from his blood in the seventeenth century. At this time transfusions were first attempted, and since few men would volunteer their own circulatory fluid, the lamb became the animal of choice. Blood of man and beast were never meant to mix, as many a sick or dying patient would surely have attested, for as soon as they were joined, a clumping together of cells occurred which prevented their further usefulness. The red blood cells could no longer carry sufficient oxygen. Probably only those receiving small volumes lived to tell of it.

In the 1800s transfusion of blood from man to man was practiced, sometimes with striking and miraculous success. Again, and most unfortunately, there were those who achieved only pain and tingling sensations and others who died at once. It was learned that the blood of certain men causes clumping of cells in certain other men. Patients surviving this might die of infection transmitted from dirty surgeons and dirty instruments.

Not until the year 1901 did a really scientific basis exist for the transfusion of blood. It was recognized at this time that blood must be divided into groups, or types and that only certain definite types could be transfused successfully to any given individual. This grouping procedure, combined with the discovery of good anti-clotting agents and surgical sanitation, has made blood transfusion a modern symbol of life.

**Why and when to transfuse.** An accident occurs and the victim is brought into the hospital, crushed and bleeding. His blood pressure is low; his pulse rapid and weak. Blue-tinted lips indicate an inability of the blood to carry enough oxygen, strongly suggesting a transfusion. Upon receipt of the properly typed blood, the patient's appearance and responsiveness will be much improved. All the functions of his own blood will be immediately taken over by that of the donor, unless his condition is quite severe.

Transfusions are advised in all cases where one or more liters (1 liter=about 2 pints) of the body's five liters of blood are lost and are helpful also in less obvious circumstances. Some hospitals routinely administer blood before and after all major operations, having shown lower mortality and speedier recovery where this is done. The patients benefited have not always suffered actual blood loss.

"Bleeders," those individuals suffering from *hemophilia,* sometimes require numerous transfusions. Their blood will not clot. Simple tooth extraction becomes major surgery for them, and small wounds leak like sieves. Blood from another donor is especially important since it contains the elements essential for clotting.

Burn cases require special treatment. Large quantities of fluid escape through the charred areas but only small numbers of the actual red blood cells. The concentrated, sluggish, reduced circulatory flow speeds again when *plasma,* blood's fluid minus the cells, is transfused.

**Blood substitutes.** A single B-29 flying over Hiroshima dropped the bomb which signaled the end of World War II, but a new problem prevailed. Sixty per cent or more of the Japanese injured by nuclear blasts had burns, and many others were crushed and cut. Blood transfusions for such large numbers of victims are impossible in wartime and difficult even in less severe peacetime emergencies. The challenge to researchers in blood substitutes has been tremendous.

The use of plasma has helped in the past. Plasma lacks red cells and can be pooled to dilute other factors which promote clumping of the recipient's blood cells. For this reason it can be transfused more or less indiscriminately. In a frozen or dried state it can be stored indefinitely, retaining all the good qualities of blood except the ability to transport oxygen. Water added to the dried product restores it to its normal condition. However, plasma is derived from whole blood, and there still exists the problem of solicitation from donors.

Saline solution (made by adding 0.9 gm. table salt to 100 ml. water) is occasionally used for blood replacement. Unfortunately the molecules of salt are small. Most of them leak from the blood vessels almost as quickly as put in, therefore having little permanent value.

A sugar solution called *dextran* is employed with somewhat more success. The larger size of its molecules prevents escape through the microscopic pores of the capillaries.

Rather surprisingly, massive injections of *vitamin C* effectively combat some types of severe bleeding and circulatory failure in rabbits, cats, and guinea pigs. The exact physiological reaction is unknown but perhaps results from alterations of oxygen utilization within the cells themselves.

**Blood types and transfusion safety.** Usually all that the patient sees of blood typing is the puncture of a finger and the removal of two or three drops of blood. Behind the scenes there is a man in a white coat who mixes this blood with other blood and observes them under the microscope. By noting which sample bloods show clumping together of cells, or, as he calls it, *"agglutination,"* he obtains the blood type. With this information, and perhaps that of other simple tests, he learns from whom the patient may safely receive blood and for whom he may safely donate blood.

Four basic types of blood are known: *A, B, AB,* and *O,* the letters representing the presence or absence of particular agglutinating agents in the red blood cells. Safety ordinarily prescribes (with certain exceptions in emergencies) that only A blood be transfused to A blood, B blood to B blood, and so forth. If one mistakenly adds type A to type B blood, it agglutinates (clumps). This results from the presence of an *anti-A* chemical in the plasma of type B individuals. Similarly, type A blood has an *anti-B* plasma chemical. Obviously type AB blood has neither anti-A nor anti-B factors or the person's blood cells would fatally clump together. Type O blood (which has neither A nor B blood cells) has both anti-A and anti-B chemicals in the plasma.

Table 1.    THE BLOOD TYPES

| A person in group: | has this type of red blood cells: | and this type of plasma: |
|---|---|---|
| A | A | anti-B |
| B | B | anti-A |
| AB | AB | no anti plasma |
| O | O | anti-A and anti-B |

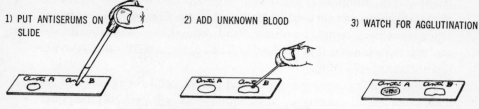

1) PUT ANTISERUMS ON SLIDE    2) ADD UNKNOWN BLOOD    3) WATCH FOR AGGLUTINATION

Fig. 37–1 PROCEDURE FOR TYPING BLOOD

The Rh factors, first reported in 1940, are also typed before transfusions. These are weaker agglutinating substances (Rh$^+$) found in eighty-five per cent of the white population and to a greater extent in other races. Rh negatives do not have this agglutinating material in their blood.

## HOW TO TYPE BLOOD

Select a clean microscope slide and mark it as illustrated in Fig. 37–1. Add a drop of antiserum A to one side of the slide and a drop of antiserum B to the other side. With alcohol, cleanse your finger or that of a friend. Puncture the fingertip with a sterile needle or blade (such as Hemolets described in Chapter 34). Allow one or two drops of blood to accumulate. With a toothpick, transfer a small quantity of blood to antiserum A. Using another toothpick, transfer blood to antiserum B. This must be done quickly before the blood has a chance to coagulate.

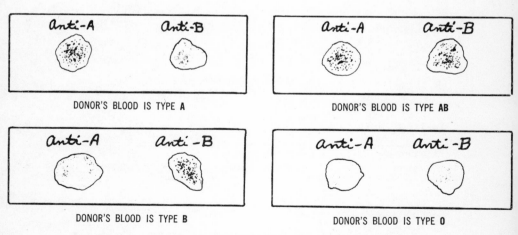

| anti-A | anti-B | anti-A | anti-B |
| DONOR'S BLOOD IS TYPE **A** | | DONOR'S BLOOD IS TYPE **AB** | |

| anti-A | anti-B | anti-A | anti-B |
| DONOR'S BLOOD IS TYPE **B** | | DONOR'S BLOOD IS TYPE **O** | |

Fig. 37–2 REACTION OF ANTISERUMS WITH VARIOUS BLOOD TYPES

Allow several minutes for agglutination to occur. Observe this first with the unaided eye and then under the microscope. Fig. 37–2 shows which types react with which antiserums and follows the rules already described. For example, type A blood will be agglutinated by anti-A serum but not by anti-B serum.

If you try this experiment on several people, total the results and see how many are of each type. Most individuals will probably be either type A or O. The distribution of these two groups is about equal in large populations.

A word of caution! Type determinations by inexperienced persons are not always accurate. Only those obtained by physicians and trained technicians should be considered in transfusion work.

## OTHER THINGS TO DO
Blood typing has entered the field of legal medicine. It may aid in spotting suspected criminals or uncovering a baby's actual parents (since blood groups are inherited). Of equal or greater importance is the detection of blood itself, as opposed to catsup or red ink. You may perform this analysis by using a saturated solution of benzidine in glacial acetic acid. Add three drops to an equal quantity of the solution to be tested. Now add a drop of three per cent hydrogen peroxide. Hemoglobin of blood decomposes hydrogen peroxide, yielding oxygen which chemically reacts with benzidine to give a blue or green color. Try dilute solutions of blood to show the extreme sensitivity of this test.

# The Lungs

## 38
## LIFE-GIVING LUNGS

**Materials.**
1. Lungs and windpipe of a large animal
2. Source of compressed air
3. Bell jar, two balloons, one-hole rubber stopper, Y-tube, adhesive tape, string, and sheet of latex rubber

**Role of the ribs and diaphragm.** The diaphragm contracts and the ribs ascend. Air sucks in quickly to fill the vacancy. There is no choice with a vacuum in the chest. The lungs must inflate.

What is the *diaphragm?* It is the inside, dome-shaped sheet of muscle separating the chest from the abdomen. During inhalation the muscle contracts and draws the diaphragm downward. Other muscles, those of the chest wall, called *intercostals,* move the ribs upward and outward. It is this combined action which expands the chest cavity. Without muscles the lungs are completely helpless.

Normal exhalation is passive. The muscles relax and the ribs and diaphragm return to their original position. During exercise, however, air must be driven out of the lungs more quickly. Another set of inter-costal muscles contracts, pulling the ribs down and in. The abdominal muscles tense and force the diaphragm up.

**The lungs and respiratory tract (Fig. 38–1).** The spongy, elastic lungs entirely fill the *pleural,* or chest cavity. Each lung is divided into lobes. In man there are two lobes on the left and three lobes on the right.

Air rushing lungward must pass through numerous smaller and smaller tubes before reaching its destination. It gets started, of course, in the nasal cavities and then travels through the *pharynx* to the *larynx,* or

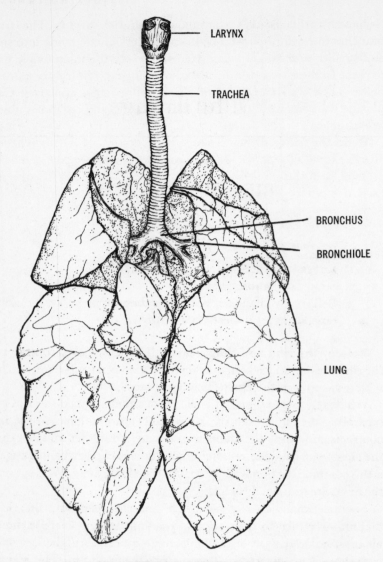

LARYNX

TRACHEA

BRONCHUS

BRONCHIOLE

LUNG

Fig. 38–1 THE LUNGS AND TRACHEA OF A HOG

voice box. (The vocal cords are found here. The "Adam's apple" is a cartilage of the larynx.) There is an opening here guarded by the flap-like *epiglottis* which prevents food and water from getting into the respiratory passageways when we swallow.

Air now flows through the windpipe, or *trachea,* a tube lined with

C-shaped cartilages and continuous with the larynx. The trachea branches into two *bronchi,* one to each lung. These divide into smaller and smaller *bronchioles* which lead to *alveoli,* the microscopic goal of oxygen. In these tiny sacs the actual exchange of respiratory gases takes place. Their walls are in contact with pulmonary capillaries. Carbon dioxide transfers from the blood to the alveoli, and oxygen is absorbed in exchange.

**Dead air space.** When we breathe in, not all of the air reaches the alveoli. Some of it must fill up the air passageways: the trachea, the bronchi, and the bronchioles. Since it does not function in the actual exchange of oxygen and carbon dioxide, it is called the *dead air space.*

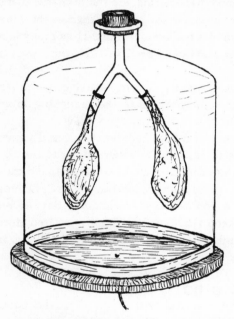

Fig. 38–2 DIAPHRAGM AND LUNG MODEL

**Making a model of the diaphragm and lungs (Fig. 38–2).** Fit a one-hole rubber stopper with a Y-tube and attach it to a bell jar or gallon jug with the bottom cut off. Attach a balloon to each arm of the Y. Through the middle of a sheet of latex rubber, knot a string and tie off the opening. The rubber membrane, which should now be taped to the bottom of the jar, illustrates the diaphragm. The partially inflated balloons represent the lungs. Pull on the string. The lowered diaphragm decreases the pressure in the jar, causing the outside air to rush in through the passageways to the balloons. Release the string. This causes the diaphragm to relax, and air passes out of the balloons. To illustrate active expiration, push up on the diaphragm. This increase in pressure forces air out, and the balloons collapse.

## EXAMINING AND INFLATING AN ANIMAL'S LUNGS

Visit your local slaughterhouse and purchase the lungs of an animal. Specify that the trachea be left intact. Wash out as much blood as possible. Do you notice how the lungs float in water? Once an animal takes its first breath, gases in the alveoli can never be completely forced out. Only the lungs of unborn animals will sink.

Examine the spongy tissue. Imagine the immense surface which this involves. The area available for air exchange in the human lungs approximates the area of a badminton court. How many lobes are present in the lungs of your particular specimen? Are the same number present on both sides?

Feel the tough C-shaped pieces of cartilage in the trachea. Follow them up to the larynx and down to the branching bronchi. Study as many of the smaller passageways as are visible.

You may permanently inflate and dry the animal's lung if you have a source of compressed air. Attach rubber tubing to the air outlet. Insert glass tubing of an appropriate size into the animal's trachea. Join the tubes and turn on a gentle continuous flow of air. The lungs will inflate. Let air continue to flow through for about a day, or until they have definitely dried. Keep the lungs maximally inflated during this time. When you have finished, cut off a small piece of lung and inspect its holey appearance.

## OTHER THINGS TO DO

More instructive, but less permanent than the balloon model of respiration, is a model made with real lungs. You may use those which you later dry and inflate. Connect them to a tube inserted through the rubber stopper. Now pull down the rubber diaphragm of your model. The lungs expand exactly as they do in the living animal.

As a reference on respiratory physiology, we recommend an article by W. O. Fenn, "The mechanism of breathing," *Scientific American*, 202:138, January 1960. One of the illustrations shows a cast made by pouring liquid plastic into the trachea, then dissolving away the lung tissue. The plastic has penetrated hundreds of tiny bronchioles to expose the vast extent of the mammalian gas exchange system.

# 39
# VOLUMES AND RATES OF BREATHING

**Materials.**
1. A one-gallon bottle and quart milk bottle
2. Empty aquarium or dishpan
3. One-inch (or one-half inch) diameter rubber hose
4. One-inch (or one-half inch) diameter polyethylene tubing
5. Gas or dust mask
6. Adhesive tape
7. Beach ball
8. Watch or clock with second hand

**The importance of adequate respiration.** Step outside on some early summer morning. Breathe in the fresh, cool air. Invigorating, isn't it? This is an atmosphere of health and life. Breathing is not so refreshing for all people. Some have asthma or other respiratory ailments. Their air passageways will not open wide enough. They feel as an ordinary person feels if he breathes through a narrow piece of glass tubing. Air is hard to suck in. In mild cases this is apparent only during activity when it is necessary to breathe rapidly and deeply. In very serious diseases patients must gasp each breath, even when they lie perfectly still.

Seldom do we think of inhaling and exhaling. The brain and lungs do the task without our help. Yet, how vital is this air. Without it, unconsciousness and death occur in minutes. The physician realizes the importance of respiratory volumes. With a few simple instruments he can quickly detect disorders of the respiratory system. Proper treatment may bring prompt relief.

**Normal volumes and rate of breathing.** About 500 cubic centimeters (one pint) of air are drawn in or exhaled with each breath. This value is called the *tidal volume* (Fig. 39–1). The average respiratory rate is sixteen breaths per minute, but this varies greatly in different individuals. Usually when the rate is high, the tidal volume is low, and vice versa.

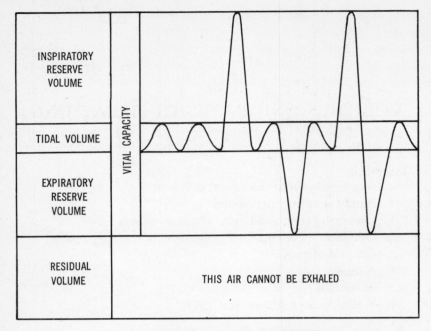

Fig. 39–1 THE RESPIRATORY VOLUMES

Respiratory physiologists frequently use the words *inspire* as synonymous with inhale and *expire* for exhale.

Pause a moment! Take a normal breath. Now, continue to inhale as deeply as possible. If you are an average person you have inspired an extra two liters (two quarts) of air. This air is called the *inspiratory reserve volume*.

Now try this! Breathe out a normal breath. Continue exhaling until all of your air is exhausted. This volume beyond a normal expiration is called the *expiratory reserve volume*. Normally this is about one and one-half liters of air.

One more test! Take a very deep breath. Hold it! Now exhale the entire volume of air. The volume of air just expired is called the *vital capacity*. This is about four liters (one gallon) for men and three liters for women. The vital capacity represents the total inspiratory reserve volume, tidal volume, and expiratory reserve volume.

No matter how big-winded you are, you will never force all the air from the lungs. The lungs adhere closely to the chest wall, and ribs prevent the chest from completely collapsing. This volume of air which remains in the lungs after maximal expiration is called the *residual volume*. It normally amounts to about one and one-half liters.

**Minute volume.** The volume of air breathed in (or out) in one minute is called the *minute volume*. This is about six to eight liters in a resting adult man. The most accurate method for obtaining minute volume is to collect and measure all of the air exhaled in one or more minutes. Another method would be to obtain a measurement of tidal volume and multiply this by the respiratory rate.

**The effects of exercise on breathing.** Ping-pong, horseshoes, croquet—even very light activity causes the volume of air breathed to double or triple. The change in respiration is usually not noticed except during very hard exercise. At such times the minute volume may increase from six or eight to over 100 liters per minute (Fig. 39–2).

Respiratory volume changes are affected by both rate and depth of breathing. With violent exercise the rate may be fifty breaths per minute, while the depth increases from one-half to two liters.

**Physical fitness and respiration.** Athletes usually show a greater depth of breathing and a slower rate. Training enables them to use more of their lung capacity. During exercise the physically fit show less distress and recover more quickly than do their non-physically fit friends.

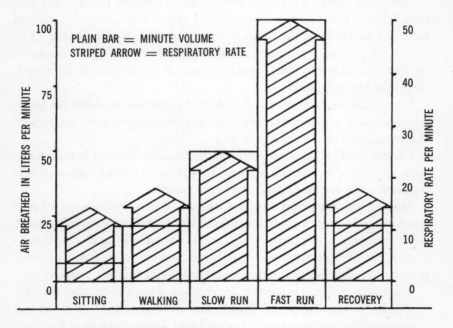

Fig. 39–2 MINUTE VOLUMES AND RESPIRATORY RATES DURING EXERCISE

The muscles of trained athletes show greater mechanical efficiency. This indicates improved economy of oxygen usage. The physically fit can perform for a longer period of time even when their minute volumes are no greater than those of the unfit.

The vital capacity of athletes is usually larger than that of non-athletes. Increases occur in untrained individuals only when they are exposed to prolonged conditioning programs.

**Oxygen consumption.** There is a direct relation between minute volume, oxygen consumption, and work performance. Exercise increases the need for oxygen. The respiratory rate and depth increase to supply this oxygen.

## HOW TO MEASURE RESTING AIR VOLUMES

Obtain a one-gallon bottle. Fill it with one liter of water from a volumetric flask (or with a quart from a quart bottle). Make a mark or place a strip of adhesive tape at the one-liter level. Continue filling the bottle with water, making a mark after each liter (or quart). A one-gallon bottle holds about four liters. Invert the filled bottle in a deep pan of water. Take care not to include any air bubbles. This can be accomplished by covering the mouth with a glass plate.

Now get a two-foot length of large-diameter rubber tubing (one-half inch is fine), and you are ready for the test. Take a deep breath and blow out all air from the lungs through the tube into the bottle (Fig. 39-3). Determine the volume of air expired by checking the marks on the bottle. This is your vital capacity. Very windy people will completely empty the bottle of water.

Obtain the inspiratory reserve volume by inhaling air from the bottle when no water is in it. Take a deep breath following normal inspiration. Water will rush in as air is drawn out.

Fill the bottle with water once again. Expire a normal breath. Continue to expire, letting this air pass through the rubber tube and into the bottle. This is your expiratory reserve volume.

**Minute volumes and exercise effects.** To measure minute volumes you will need a large airtight bag in which only expired air is collected. A beach ball makes an excellent bag, and the valving system of an Army-surplus gas or dust mask allows only exhaled air to escape. The inexpensive M1 dust respirator is particularly good for this purpose.

The beach ball and respirator are connected with each other through one inch (or one-half inch) plastic and rubber tubings (Fig. 39-4). Cut a small hole at one end of the ball and insert a five-inch length of

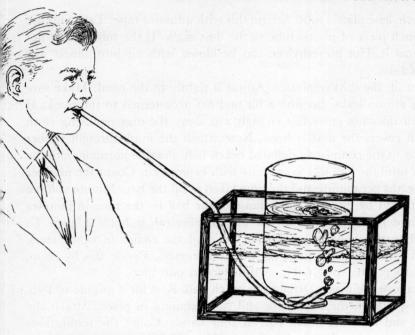

Fig. 39–3 METHOD FOR MEASURING RESPIRATORY VOLUMES

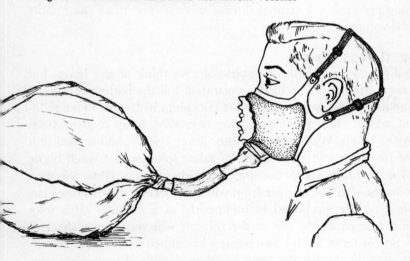

Fig. 39–4 APPARATUS FOR MEASURING MINUTE VOLUMES

polyethylene plastic tube. Secure this with adhesive tape. Tape another five-inch piece of plastic tube to the dust mask. If the tubing does not fit, heat it. Hot polyethylene can be blown with air into almost any desired size.

Put on the dust respirator. Adjust it tightly to the head. Make sure there are no leaks. Breathe a bit and get accustomed to the mask. If the air does not enter fast enough, cut away the dust-removing cloth which covers the mask's front. Now attach the mask through rubber tubing to the completely deflated beach ball. Breathe normally into the mask until the ball fills to capacity with expired air. Count the number of breaths per minute and the time taken to fill the bag. Minute volume is obtained by dividing the volume of the ball by the time in minutes required to fill the bag. If the ball is spherical, it holds $4/3\pi r^3$. To translate this volume into liters, first find the radius in centimeters. Then calculate the volume in cubic centimeters. Divide this by 1000, since there are 1000 cubic centimeters in one liter.

Remove the mask. Deflate the beach ball. Rest for a minute or two.

Now put on the dust mask and start running in place. Attach the mask and hold the beach ball in your hands. Count the respirations and the time required to fill the bag. Note that the rate and depth of breathing are greatly increased during exercise. Calculate the minute and tidal volumes.

## OTHER THINGS TO DO

Usually when we think of respiration, we think of the lungs, but tissue respiration may also be demonstrated. Fill the bottom of a small wide-mouthed bottle with one gram of potassium hydroxide in ten milliliters of water. (Potassium hydroxide is caustic. Keep it away from clothing or hands. Wash off with water if any spills.) Add several thin slices of frog liver and a few drops of saline solution to a small bottle lid and float this on the potassium hydroxide solution. Close the flask with a one-hole rubber stopper from which projects a very narrow glass tube or a pipette graduated in hundredths of a milliliter. If a soap bubble is formed at the top of the tube, it will very slowly descend (allow one or more hours) as oxygen is consumed by the liver. Potassium hydroxide absorbs the tissue's carbon dioxide. In principle, this reaction duplicates the mouse metabolism measurement of Chapter 28.

# 40

# THE CARBON DIOXIDE STORY

**Materials.**

1. Half-pint bottle or beaker
2. Sodium hydroxide, phenolphthalein
3. Glass or plastic tube

**Carbon dioxide aboard submarines.** In the early days of submarine warfare, crowded crews breathed only the air trapped inside their vessels. To get more, they surfaced. Even in peacetime the absence of ventilation proved hazardous, as illustrated by the S-4 which sank off Provincetown, Massachusetts, in 1927. The crew tapped out messages to rescue ships stationed 160 feet above. Compressed air was sacrificed in an attempt to blow out the ballast tanks, but this failed. A storm prevented divers from connecting an air line with another ship. When finally reached, the entire crew of forty had suffocated.

If submarines must stay submerged for long periods without continuous air supplements, the crews are requested to limit their activities and sometimes to lie quietly in their bunks. This reduces the body's energy needs and hence, the volumes of air respired. A decrease in the ship's oxygen is not as dangerous as the accompanying rise of carbon dioxide emptied from the lungs. The latter gas, when it has increased to five or six per cent, causes the breathing to become very deep and labored. Headache and nausea develop, making the condition more unpleasant. Ten per cent carbon dioxide is the absolute maximum tolerated. This raises the volume of air respired from a normal eight to an abnormal seventy liters per minute. Higher concentrations depress breathing and eventually produce unconsciousness and death.

Today's submarines air out with snorkles. In addition, soda lime, lithium hydroxide, or other carbon dioxide absorbents, and oxygen tanks are usually provided for emergencies. Microscopic plants have been suggested as air purifiers for extreme depths during prolonged travels.

Manned space satellites and rockets, however, are more likely to employ such plants.

**Carbon dioxide treatment of respiratory depression.** The stimulant action of carbon dioxide makes it useful for reviving patients with an acute deficiency of oxygen. Usually five per cent of the gas is mixed with ninety-five per cent oxygen. This combination has been especially beneficial for carbon monoxide poisoning. The deeper, more rapid respirations aid the patient in breathing off the poisonous gas.

**Reductions of carbon dioxide.** The quantity of carbon dioxide in the blood can be reduced by forced, rapid breathing in a resting individual. This is often followed by slowing or temporary cessation of breathing. The carbon dioxide produced by the tissues gradually recollects and once again stimulates respiration.

In certain heart and kidney diseases the breathing centers of the brain become less sensitive to the carbon dioxide normally present in the blood. In such cases, the respiration may become periodic. There are alternate periods of no breathing (from reduced sensitivity to carbon dioxide) followed by periods of rapid and deep breathing (from accumulation of carbon dioxide).

**Formation and disposal of carbon dioxide.** Carbohydrates, fats, and proteins are constantly breaking down in the body to provide energy for heat and motion. Carbon dioxide, a by-product of this breakdown, is transported from the tissues to the lungs by the blood. Normally, about four per cent carbon dioxide is present in air exhaled from the lungs. During exercise the quantity of the gas produced increases, but only small amounts accumulate inside the body. Rapid, deep breathing gets rid of the rest.

## HOW TO DETECT THE CARBON DIOXIDE OF YOUR BREATH

Dissolve one gram of sodium hydroxide in 100 milliliters of water. Transfer fifteen drops of this solution into the bottom of a half-pint bottle or similar small container. Add fifty milliliters of water and a pinch or a few drops of phenolphthalein. The solution will turn red, indicating that it is alkaline.

Breathe normally through a glass or plastic tube into the solution. Inhale through the nose but exhale directly into the bottle. Carbon dioxide becomes carbonic acid in the presence of water. This neutralizes the sodium hydroxide and gradually causes the phenolphthalein indicator to turn pink and then colorless. Record the time taken for the solution to become completely colorless.

Empty and then refill the bottle with the same volume and strength of sodium hydroxide and phenolphthalein. Perform some rapid, vigorous exercise. Stop and immediately start expiring into the second red solution. Record the time it takes to become colorless. The time should be shortened because of the greater quantity of $CO_2$ exhaled during exercise.

## OTHER THINGS TO DO

Here is a simple way to show how carbon dioxide speeds respiration. Count your normal, resting respiratory rate; then breathe directly into an unperforated plastic refrigerator bag or paper sack. Continue this for several minutes or until breathing becomes difficult. Measure the respiratory rate at approximately the middle and end of this period. Does the frequency increase as carbon dioxide accumulates? Watch also for a greater depth of breathing.

4I

# BREATH HOLDING

**Materials.**
1. Watch or clock with second hand

**Control of respiration during exercise (Fig. 41–1).** Swimming under water . . . almost there. Your lungs seem ready to burst. You choke down a gasp; then, up through the water quickly. Inhale the reviving air. What forces you to come up? Why do you breathe so heavily? If you answer, *carbon dioxide,* your suspicions are justified. This gas intensifies until it finally compels respiration. It acts by exciting *breathing centers* of the *medulla* (lower brain). It also provokes respiratory impulses from the *chemoreceptor* nerves of the carotid arteries of the neck and of the aortic arch. These are the same receptors which augment the functions of our circulatory system.

There are other factors regulating suspended respiration and the respiration of exercise. Chiefly these are: (1) oxygen deficits, (2) muscular contractions, and (3) emotions. *Oxygen shortages* encourage faster, deeper breathing through their influence on the chemoreceptors. *Muscle contractions* transmit impulses along nerves to the medulla's respiratory centers. These impulses make the brain more responsive to carbon dioxide excess and oxygen lack. Anger, fear, joy, and other *emotions* act similarly by keeping the breathing centers keyed up. During the balloon ascent through a thunderstorm mentioned earlier, the passengers experienced respiratory rates higher than seventy breaths per minute.

**Resting control of respiration.** As the lungs collapse when one exhales, messages are sent through nerves to the medulla's breathing centers. These stop expiration and cause the lungs to inflate. The expanded lungs stretch nerve receptors which again send out impulses to the brain. Inflation stops and deflation starts. This cycle continues throughout a lifetime.

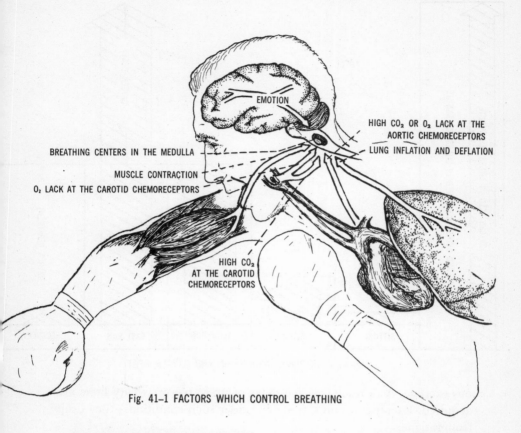

EMOTION

HIGH CO₂ OR O₂ LACK AT THE
AORTIC CHEMORECEPTORS

LUNG INFLATION AND DEFLATION

BREATHING CENTERS IN THE MEDULLA

MUSCLE CONTRACTION

O₂ LACK AT THE CAROTID CHEMORECEPTORS

HIGH CO₂
AT THE CAROTID
CHEMORECEPTORS

Fig. 41–1 FACTORS WHICH CONTROL BREATHING

**Exercise and oxygen debt (Fig. 41–2).** At rest or during light activity plenty of oxygen is breathed into the body to meet tissue demands. Physiologists call this the *"steady state."* The steadiness, however, is briefly disrupted when one starts a somewhat more strenuous exercise. To re-establish a balance, the respiration and circulation accelerate, bringing in more oxygen, and this happens even as the exercise continues. Very severe exertion prevents the establishment of a balance. In this case, the individual is said to have an *oxygen debt.* Eventually he must slow down because of the insufficiency of oxygen. To repay the debt, the breathing and circulatory output remains high for minutes or even hours after exercise.

Normally, only about one-fourth liter of oxygen is consumed in one minute. With activity the oxygen consumption may increase to three or four liters per minute, and even this is not enough during very labori-

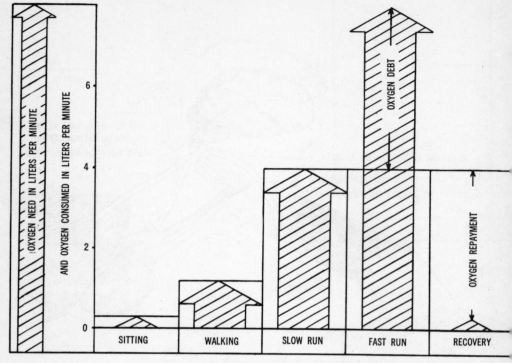

Fig. 41-2 OXYGEN CONSUMPTION AND OXYGEN DEBT

ous exercise. As a result, oxygen debts of up to ten or twenty liters are acquired. Exercisers cannot function under such conditions; they drop from fatigue.

## LIMITS OF BREATH HOLDING (Fig. 41–3)

Take a deep inspiration, then see how long you can hold it. If you rank among the average, you will suspend respiration for only one-half to one minute. By this time carbon dioxide overwhelms the breathing centers and you gulp down a sizable whiff of air.

Wait a few minutes. Take several very deep breaths, then cease breathing again. Does this help improve your performance? The inspirations brought in a little reserve of oxygen, but more important was the discharge of excess carbon dioxide during the expirations. Do not continue the overbreathing for a long period of time. Dizziness or cramps will result.

Rest again. Now hold your breath after a maximal expiration. The time is shorter, isn't it? Oxygen is used up rapidly from your circulatory

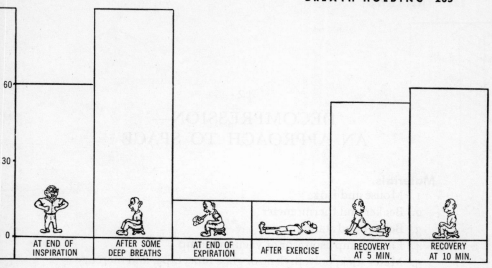

Fig. 41-3 FACTORS WHICH ALTER BREATH HOLDING

system and collapsed lungs, and carbon dioxide accumulates just as rapidly.

Start running in place or perform some other strenuous exercise. Do this as fast as possible for one minute. Time the duration of breath holding immediately after and at five and ten minutes after this exercise. A gradual recovery will be noted.

## OTHER THINGS TO DO

Exhaled air has a meager content of oxygen, a fact which you may very simply demonstrate. Float a lighted candle beneath an inverted jar. Notice how long it takes to burn out and how far the water rises to replace oxygen as it is consumed. Relight the candle. Place it under the same bottle after completely filling the bottle with exhaled air. The candle flickers and goes out quickly. We conclude that part of the oxygen has been used up, since air leaving the lungs will not support a flame.

# 42

# DECOMPRESSION—
# AN APPROACH TO SPACE

**Materials.**
1. Mouse and frog
2. Beaker and thermometer
3. Bell jar and stand
4. Filter pump aspirator or vacuum pump
5. Meter stick, polyethylene or glass tube, tape, and mercury

**Ascent of the Zenith balloon.** Everything seemed O.K. There was oxygen aboard. The three Frenchmen were well dressed for cold at high altitudes. Yet three hours later, two lay dead in the basket beneath the balloon. The survivor, Tissandier, told the story of this eventful day . . . April 15, 1875. This is his record of the peak ascent.*

"I come to the fatal hour when we are about to be seized by the terrible influence of atmospheric decompression. At 7000 meters (23,000 feet) we are all standing in the basket; Sivel, numbed for a moment, has revived; Croce-Spinelli is motionless in front of me . . . my hands were cold, icy. I wanted to put on my fur gloves; but without realizing it, the action of taking them from my pocket demanded an effort which I could no longer make. . . . Toward 7500 meters . . . the body and mind weaken . . . without one's knowledge. One does not suffer at all . . . one becomes indifferent; one no longer thinks of the perilous situation or of the danger; one rises and is happy to rise. . . . Soon I wanted to seize the oxygen tube but could not raise my arm. . . . I wanted to cry out, 'We are at 8000 meters!' But my tongue was paralyzed. Suddenly I closed my eyes and fell inert, entirely losing consciousness."

Instruments showed that the Zenith reached 28,000 feet before coming down. During descent Croce awoke and threw out ballast, not

* From a translation of Paul Bert's, *La pression barometrique,* 1878. M. A. Hitchcock and F. A. Hitchcock, *Bert's Barometric Pressure,* College Book Company, Columbus, Ohio, 1943.

recognizing their plight. Oxygen lack dulled his senses. They rose again, this time to death. Only Tissandier recovered. His vivid account assured that no human would again approach these altitudes except with caution and the continuous use of oxygen.

**Classification of hypoxias.** Any condition of deficient oxygen is called *hypoxia,* or anoxia. There are four types of hypoxia. These are: (1) hypoxic hypoxia, (2) anemic hypoxia, (3) stagnant hypoxia, and (4) histotoxic hypoxia.

*Hypoxic hypoxia* results when the oxygen deficiency is in the lungs. This develops at high altitudes or when the lungs or respiratory passageways are damaged. The subject becomes weak, lightheaded, and eventually looses consciousness as did the Zenith balloon passengers. The feeling is not unpleasant, and often the subject does not recognize that he has fainted. In fact, he may deny it vehemently. In Fig. 42–1 we show a typical account written during oxygen deprivation. Notice the increasingly poor handwriting as unconsciousness approaches.

*Anemic hypoxia* results from insufficient oxygen in the blood. Hemorrhage (blood loss) or anemia (hemoglobin or red blood cell deficiency) are good examples. Less oxygen is carried with less blood or hemoglobin. Carbon monoxide poisoning also involves a diminished blood oxygen. Hemoglobin has a much stronger affinity for carbon monoxide than for oxygen. As a result, little oxygen will be circulated in the presence of this poisonous gas.

*Stagnant hypoxia* results from a slowed circulation. The more sluggishly the blood moves, the less effectively can it carry oxygen about the body. Shock and heart failure act by this means.

*Histotoxic hypoxia* is a form which acts in the body tissues. The cells receive sufficient oxygen but cannot utilize it. Cyanide poisoning is a type of histotoxic hypoxia.

**Problems of the aviator.** Modern oxygen and pressurization equipment eliminate most of the difficulties of those who travel by air. Oxygen is supplied at altitudes of 10,000 feet in most commercial vehicles. Few, if any, symptoms are noted at lesser altitudes.

Commercial air travelers are not exposed to this problem, but aviators sometimes get the "bends," or *aeroembolism* when they ascend to 30,000 or 35,000 feet without sealed or pressurized enclosures. Divers also get the bends when they surface with haste from great depths. The problem arises when nitrogen bubbles form in the blood because of the reduction of air or water pressure. The bubble formation is similar to that seen when the lid of a pop bottle is removed, thereby exposing

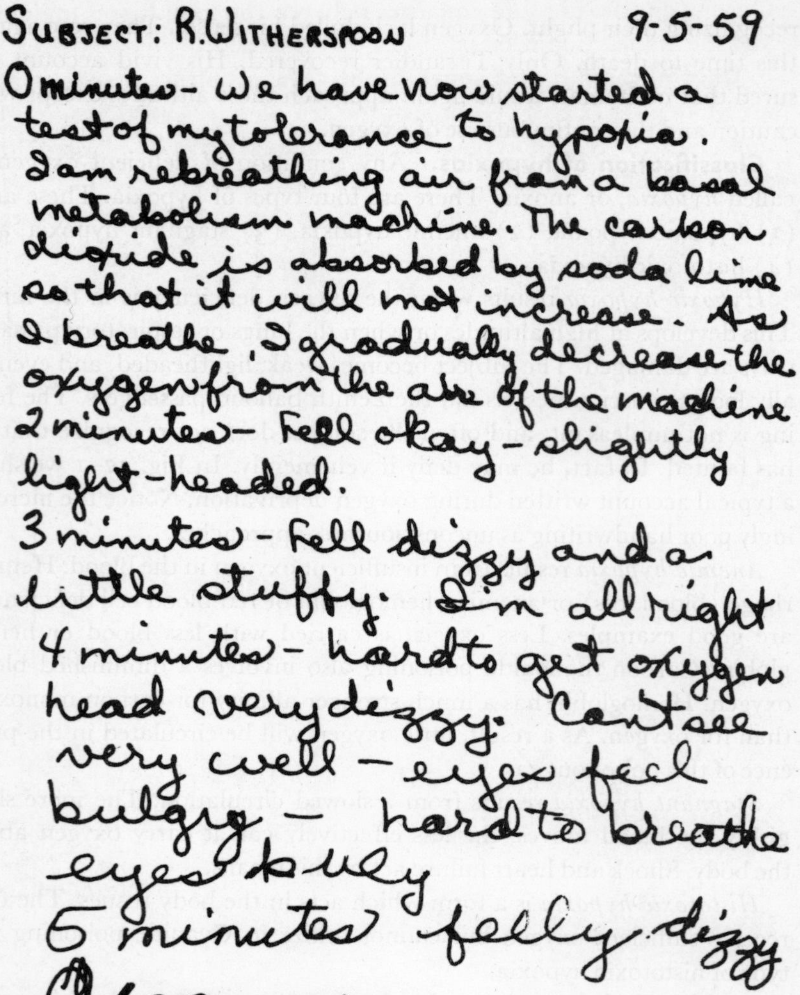

SUBJECT: R. WITHERSPOON                9-5-59

0 minutes - We have now started a test of my tolerance to hypopia. I am rebreathing air from a basal metabolism machine. The carbon dioxide is absorbed by soda lime so that it will not increase. As I breathe, I gradually decrease the oxygen from the air of the machine

2 minutes - Feel okay - slightly light-headed.

3 minutes - Feel dizzy and a little stuffy. I'm all right

4 minutes - hard to get oxygen head very dizzy. Can't see very well - eyes feel bulging - hard to breathe eyes bulgy

5 minutes felly dizzy

Witherspoon

Fig. 42-1 RECORD OF A SUBJECT DURING OXYGEN DEPRIVATION

the fluid inside to a lesser pressure. The aeroembolism bubbles cause pain, especially at the joints.

Perhaps you have noticed a very full feeling in the ears while driving down a mountain or steep hill. Aviators of non-pressurized aircraft experience similar sensations. The middle ear is connected by a small tube (Eustachian tube) to the back of the mouth. Pressure builds up in the middle ear during descent until it is difficult to open this tube.

Once open, the pressure equalizes between the mouth and middle ear, and the fullness diminishes.

**Decompression and space flight.** The problems of space travelers are more intense than are those of the aeronaut. On earth we sometimes must face oxygen shortages, but in the void between planets there is no oxygen at all, and even at 50,000 feet the atmosphere is so rare that it must be considered the physiological equivalent of space. If the lid blows off a satellite, or if a meteor comes plummeting through it, there will be plenty of trouble. The pressure of gas within will rapidly force air into the vacuum, just as a tire "blows out" if badly punctured. Scientists call this sudden, immediate loss of air *explosive decompression*.

The lungs also "blow out" when a space craft is punctured. Fortunately, the respiratory passageways provide a natural outlet for air expulsion. The lungs are not damaged unless an individual attempts to hold his breath. In this event, the force of decompression quickly tears holes in them.

The blood of animals and space men "boil" upon exposure to a vacuum at 63,000 feet or higher. This boiling is not associated with heat release. The reduction of pressure allows fluids to bubble at a lower temperature. In space, fluids will even boil at body temperature.

Warm-blooded animals explosively decompressed show deep, gasping respirations. The abdomen distends and mild convulsions appear. After thirty to forty seconds all of the tissues gradually swell. Animals survive such exposure if they are recompressed within one or two minutes.

Human subjects have been volunteers for explosive decompression. Such men remain conscious and capable for about twelve to fifteen seconds. It takes this long for the supply of oxygenated blood to pass from the lungs to the brain. The men pass out as soon as this supply is exhausted.

## THE APPARATUS FOR DECOMPRESSION

Ordinarily a vacuum pump is used for decompression from some enclosed chamber such as a bell jar. The pump mechanically removes air.

A much simpler and less expensive apparatus is the *filter pump water aspirator,* commonly used in chemistry laboratories to hasten filtration (Fig. 42–2). It is a T-shaped device attached to an ordinary water faucet. As water passes through the top of the T, air is sucked in at the sidearm. The suction creates a vacuum which easily allows decompression to an equivalent of 50,000 or 60,000 feet altitude.

For measuring the vacuum pressure, first heat and bend a polyethylene or glass tube into a U-shape about a meter stick, and tape the two together. Support this combination in a vertical position with the 1000 millimeter mark at the lower end. Now pour mercury into the U-shaped tube until it reaches a mark on the tube corresponding to the barometric pressure at your altitude (contact the weather bureau for the correct daily reading). As the mercury rises during decompression, the meter scale shows a lower millimeter reading (on the side connected to the vacuum source), thus indicating a drop in barometric pressure. Read the scale and compare with Table 2 to find the corresponding simulated altitude.

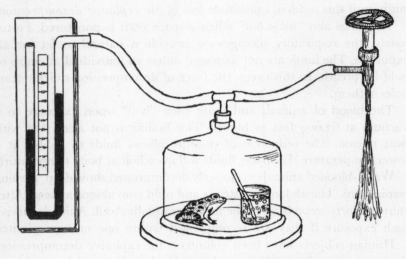

**Fig. 42-2 THE APPARATUS FOR DECOMPRESSION**

**Decompressing a mouse and a frog.** Arrange the apparatus as described above and as illustrated in Fig. 42–2. Place a mouse in the enclosed chamber. Turn on the water faucet and watch the mercury rise. Follow the altitude equivalent chart (Table 2) and find at what altitude the animal shows signs of difficult breathing or excessive movement about the enclosure. The distance in millimeters to which the mercury column rises determines the pressure. Remove the mouse when it falls unconscious. Record the pressure and altitude. The animal will revive quickly and show no aftereffects.

Perform this experiment with a frog. Cold-blooded animals require much less oxygen than do warm-blooded animals. For this reason the frog will probably show little change even after several hours of exposure.

Table 2. ALTITUDE EQUIVALENTS AT VARIOUS PRESSURES MEASURED IN MILLIMETERS OF MERCURY

| millimeters of mercury pressure | altitude in feet | millimeters of mercury pressure | altitude in feet |
|---|---|---|---|
| 760 | 0 | 215 | 31000 |
| 632 | 5000 | 206 | 32000 |
| 523 | 10000 | 196 | 33000 |
| 429 | 15000 | 187 | 34000 |
| 349 | 20000 | 179 | 35000 |
| 282 | 25000 | 141 | 40000 |
| 269 | 26000 | 111 | 45000 |
| 258 | 27000 | 87 | 50000 |
| 247 | 28000 | 69 | 55000 |
| 236 | 29000 | 43 | 65000 |
| 226 | 30000 | 34 | 70000 |

**Boiling water at a low temperature.** Warm a beaker of water to about 50°C. Place the water and a thermometer into the vacuum chamber with the frog (or in a separate container). This water will bubble and eventually boil violently as the pressure is reduced. If you have an efficient vacuum source you may reach an altitude equivalent to 63,000 feet where fluids bubble at body temperature (37°C.).

## OTHER THINGS TO DO

Did you notice changes in breathing as the mouse and the frog were decompressed? Mice particularly show an increase, both in rate and in depth. If your animals stay relatively calm, count the rate both before a test and at high altitudes. What is the importance of rapid, deep respiration at low oxygen pressures?

Compare decompression tolerance of a mouse with an animal which hibernates, e.g., a bat. Do the same for newborn or very young mice. In both bat and newborn there is an exceptional capacity to withstand high altitudes. You may wonder, as do biologists, why these animals survive for hours where others survive for only minutes. There are many current ideas, but no complete answers. Furthermore, this is just one of many unsolved problems. The research trail never ends. At each turn there is something different and intriguing. If you have started experimenting, you have started the trail. May you never turn back.

# Appendices

## Appendix A.
### THE METRIC SYSTEM OF MEASURES

The metric system, once learned, is much simpler than the one currently used in the United States. It is employed extensively in almost every civilized country except those speaking the English language. Fortunately, even here in the United States it has gained immense popularity in scientific circles.

The system is based on units of 100 and 1000. Standard prefixes such as *centi*—($\frac{1}{100}$) and *milli*—($\frac{1}{1000}$) precede each measure. For example, one metric *meter* (somewhat over a yard) contains one hundred equal and smaller units called *centimeters*. One thousandth of a meter is one *millimeter*. Similarly the metric *liter* (approximately one quart) holds 1000 *milliliters*.

We Americans do much provoking, time-consuming, mathematical juggling to convert feet to miles or gallons to cubic inches. Our European, metric-using neighbors do the same thing merely by moving a decimal point.

Common measures of the metric system and their English equivalents are listed below:

| | |
|---|---|
| 1 meter | = 100 centimeters or 1000 millimeters |
| 1 liter | = 1000 milliliters or 1000 cubic centimeters |
| 1 gram | = 1000 milligrams or 1,000,000 micrograms |
| 1 kilogram | = 1000 grams |
| 1 meter | = 3.28 feet or 39.37 inches |
| 1 liter | = 1.05 quarts |
| 1 gram | = 0.035 ounces |
| 1 kilogram | = 2.2 pounds |
| 1 inch | = 2.54 centimeters |

A nickel (coin) weighs about 5 grams.

Two level teaspoons of table salt (sodium chloride) weigh approximately 9 grams.

A tablespoon holds about 15 milliliters or ½ fluid ounce.

There are 20 drops in one milliliter of water delivered by the official U.S. medicine dropper.

One liter of water weighs 1 kilogram.

One milliliter of water weighs 1 gram.

## Appendix B.
# CENTIGRADE AND FAHRENHEIT TEMPERATURES

Generally, scientists prefer and use the centigrade (°C.) rather than the Fahrenheit (°F.) measures of temperature. The centigrade scale takes the freezing point of water as 0°C. (in place of 32°F.), and the boiling point of water as 100°C. (in place of 212°F.). Fahrenheit degrees are only 5/9 as large as centigrade degrees. In converting Fahrenheit to centigrade, we apply the formula:

$$°C. = 5/9 \ (°F. -32)$$

To change centigrade to Fahrenheit we use this formula:

$$°F. = (9/5 \times °C.) + 32$$

The average human body temperature is approximately 37°C., and room temperature is about 20 to 25° C.

## Appendix C.
# HOW BIOLOGISTS NAME ANIMALS

To avoid confusion in naming animals or plants, scientists use Latin or Greek names recognized throughout the world. To avoid further confusion, all life is classified into distinct and related groups. The largest group is called a *phylum*. As an example, Protozoa is a phylum of single-celled animals. Its name is derived from the Greek word for "first animals." Other common phyla listed in order of increasing complexity are:

1. Porifera, or sponges
2. Coelenterata, for instance, the jellyfishes
3. Platyhelminthes, or flatworms
4. Nemathelminthes, or roundworms
5. Annelida, or segmented worms
6. Mollusca, the snails, slugs, octopi, and squids
7. Arthropoda, or jointed-leg animals such as insects and crayfish
8. Echinodermata, the starfishes and sand dollars
9. Chordata, animals with a backbone or similar support

Each phylum is divided into smaller groups of related animals called *classes*. For example, fish, amphibia, reptiles, birds, and mammals are classes of the phylum Chordata. Each class is further separated into *orders*, orders into *families*, families into *genera*, and genera into *species*. A specie is usually the smallest group of animals just distinguishable from some other group.

In order to illustrate a typical classification we shall continue the breakdown for one group of the *class* Mammalia. Included in the class are animals belonging to the *order* of flesh-eaters, called carnivores—dogs, cats, bears, seals, and walruses. Dogs are one *family* of the carnivores. Coyotes and wolves belong to the same *genus* within this family but are of different *species*.

## Appendix D.
## THE CARE AND HANDLING OF FROGS AND MICE

Frogs and white mice have been selected as the chief laboratory animals of this book because they are easy to care for and are available at very reasonable prices. Frogs, for example, may be purchased at a cost of ten to twenty cents per animal from dealers in Oshkosh, Wisconsin (see Appendix E). Mice, at three for one dollar from quantity breeders (Carworth Farms, Rockland Farms, see Appendix E), are a real bargain for mammalian studies. Neither frogs nor mice are dangerous, and both require little space and not too much food.

If you require information on the maintenance of animals other than frogs or mice, we suggest that you consult E. Morholt, P. F. Brandwein, and A. Joseph, *Teaching High School Science: A Sourcebook for the Biological Sciences,* Harcourt, Brace and Company, New York, 1958, or E. J. Farris, *The Care and Breeding of Laboratory Animals,* John Wiley and Sons, Inc., New York, 1950.

**Frogs.** Frogs can conveniently be placed in the bottom of a sink into which water is allowed to run as a small stream or rapid drip. The sink must be covered to prevent their escape. Do this with screen wire or hardware cloth. Also protect the drain with screen wire. If the sink basin must be used frequently, the animals can be placed in cages at one side of the sink but must be supplied with a constant trickle of water, or leave about a quarter-inch depth of water in the bottom and change this daily. Another method frequently used is that of placing the animals in a refrigerator at 10° C. The chilled frogs move slowly and are easily handled. They may be kept this way for many weeks.

Frogs require little food, especially if placed in a cool location. If they are to be used within one or two weeks, they need not be fed. For longer periods, they should be supplied with small earthworms, larvae of various kinds, and insects. If the animals do not eat voluntarily, small pieces of liver may be put in the backs of their mouths. If their mouths are held shut, the pieces will usually be swallowed. Repeat such feedings at two-week intervals.

Frogs should not be overcrowded. At room temperature do not keep more than ten or twelve animals (medium-sized *Rana pipiens*) per square foot. Some frogs are vigorous while others show high mortality, especially during breeding seasons. Remove dead animals at once. Isolate any which develop a pinkish color of the skin, a condition commonly called "red-leg." This disease kills rapidly. It is best combated by using experimental animals as soon as possible. Alternately, a little table salt (about one level teaspoon per two quarts) or antibiotic added to the water will delay or prevent the spread of the illness.

**Mice.** Housing for mice varies considerably. Probably the best cages are those made of non-corrosive metal or plastic. These are available from several of the supply houses listed in Appendix E. Homemade wooden or wire cages are also suitable. Paint wood containers with two coats of a non-lead paint. Cover the top with screen or quarter-inch gauge wire. Cages with wire floors (use ¼-inch gauge) can be supported above newspapers to catch the droppings. Those with sheet metal or wooden floors should be filled with about a half inch of shavings (cedar reduces odors) or sawdust. The cages should contain no more than six or eight mice per square foot.

White mice are gentle creatures which do not bite unless alarmed, and such nips are always of a minor nature (treat with iodine). When raised from infancy, they become quite tame and make good pets. Handle mice by picking them up at the end of the tail. Do not hold them in the air for a needlessly long period of time. If they must be carried long distances, hold them in the palm of the hand. Handle and play with the animals frequently, as they enjoy this. Animals usually become more familiar (and lose fear) under such conditions.

Mice can be fed a diet of bread, milk, lettuce, and carrots. These items contain all the nutrients essential for their well-being. More convenient, however, especially for periods of weeks or months, is a commercially prepared feed such as the Rockland mouse diet.

Mice can be purchased as needed, but breeding of small (or large) numbers of animals is probably simpler. One male should be placed in a cage with two or three females (two months of age or older). Mating occurs during the periods of heat, every four to five days in each female. Pregnant mice may be removed to individual cages if available, but this is not essential. Each mother bears ten or twelve young in nineteen to twenty-one days. Handle the newborn as little as possible. Wean them at four weeks of age. Mother mice may be mated again as soon as their broods are weaned.

Give your animals as much water as they care to drink. This should be supplied from a water bottle attached to the side or top of each cage. Make the water outlet from quarter-inch glass or polyethylene tubing which has been heated at the end to produce an eighth-inch nozzle (Fig. D-1). Water leaves the nozzle as the mice lick it.

Clean cages once or twice weekly. Wash them out with hot, soapy water and dry completely.

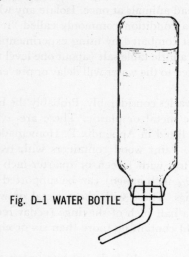

Fig. D–1 WATER BOTTLE

## Appendix E.

## · ADDRESSES OF BIOLOGICAL SUPPLY HOUSES

Many of the materials listed in this book may be purchased locally at drugstores, hardware stores, and dime stores. In addition, experiments have been selected which require commonly available animals: frogs from ponds, insects from your back yard, protozoa from ditch water. However, there are certain items most conveniently obtained from biological supply houses. One or another of the companies mentioned here can furnish whatever you want, from ordinary test tubes and white mice to specialties such as live baby coyotes and pickled whale eyes.

The prices as well as the stocks vary considerably. If you have a limited budget, it will pay to examine competitors' catalogues. Certain dealers are near a vast natural supply of living stock and can therefore make especially attractive offers. Others breed their own mice, rats, or other animals in quantity and pass on the saving.

Some of the larger companies have offices in cities throughout the United States and Canada. These are so numerous that we have named only one location for each.

| COMPANY NAME (alphabetical) | LIST OF SUPPLIES |
|---|---|
| 1. Aloe Scientific<br>5655 Kingsbury Street<br>St. Louis 12, Missouri | Blood serums, Tallqvist hemoglobin scales, blood-pressure apparatus, surgical equipment, hemocytometers, general laboratory equipment. |
| 2. American Optical Co.<br>Instrument Division<br>Buffalo 15, New York | Microscopes and accessories, eye charts, microtomes. |
| 3. Bausch & Lomb Optical Co.<br>635 St. Paul Street<br>Rochester, New York | Microscopes and accessories, projectors, eye charts, ophthalmic instruments. |
| 4. Biological Research Products Co.<br>243 West Root Street<br>Chicago 9, Illinois | Preserved organs of sheep, cattle, pigs. Brains, hearts, kidneys, lungs, livers, eyes, fetuses. |
| 5. Burdick Drosophila Supply<br>614 Evergreen Street<br>W. Lafayette, Indiana | Large variety of drosophila stocks, kits with fly food included, special ether anesthetizers. (Order two weeks before flies are needed.) |
| 6. Cambosco Scientific Co.<br>37 Antwerp Street<br>Brighton 35, Massachusetts | Laboratory equipment, chemicals, living and preserved specimens. |
| 7. Carolina Biological Supply Co.<br>Elon College, North Carolina | Large supply of living and preserved specimens, laboratory equipment, microscopes and slides, chemicals, skeletons, models. |
| 8. Carworth Farms, Inc.<br>New City, New York | Mice and rats. |
| 9. Chicago Apparatus Co.<br>1735 N. Ashland Avenue<br>Chicago 22, Illinois | Chemicals, Tallqvist hemoglobin scales, blood-pressure apparatus, hemocytometers, laboratory equipment. |
| 10. Clay-Adams Co.<br>141 E. 25th Street<br>New York 10, New York | Dissecting instruments, Tallqvist hemoglobin scales, hemocytometers, stethoscopes, tuning forks, clinical supplies. |
| 11. Denoyer-Geppert Co.<br>5235 Ravenswood Avenue<br>Chicago 40, Illinois | Microscopes and slides, charts, models, preserved specimens. |

| COMPANY NAME (alphabetical) | LIST OF SUPPLIES |
|---|---|
| 12. Fisher Scientific Supply Co.<br>139 Fisher Bldg.<br>Pittsburgh 19, Pennsylvania | Laboratory equipment, stethoscopes, microscopes, dissecting instruments. |
| 13. General Biochemicals, Inc.<br>678 Laboratory Park<br>Chagrin Falls, Ohio | Vitamin and mineral diets, hormones, enzymes, chemicals. |
| 14. General Biological Supply House, Inc. (Turtox)*<br>8200 S. Hoyne Avenue<br>Chicago 20, Illinois | Large supply of living and preserved specimens, laboratory equipment, microscopes and slides, skeletons, charts, models. |
| 15. Harlan Industries<br>Cumberland, Indiana | Mice, rats, hamsters, guinea pigs, rabbits, cages. |
| 16. Harvard Apparatus Co., Inc.<br>Dover, Massachusetts | Kymographs, inductoria, pneumographs, laboratory equipment for physiology. |
| 17. E. G. Hoffman and Son<br>P.O. Box 815<br>Oshkosh, Wisconsin | Frogs, tadpoles, turtles, crayfish, clams, necturus. |
| 18. Ideal Toy Corporation<br>184–10 Jamaica Avenue<br>Hollis 23, New York | Tyrannosaurus and other model dinosaur skeletons. |
| 19. The Lemberger Co.<br>P.O. Box 482<br>Oshkosh, Wisconsin | Frogs, turtles, pigeons, mice, rats, hamsters, guinea pigs, rabbits. |
| 20. National Biological Laboratories<br>P.O. Box 103<br>Falls Church, Virginia | Living and preserved specimens, slides, microscopes, skeletons, and models. |
| 21. Nutritional Biochemicals Corp.<br>21010 Miles Avenue<br>Cleveland 28, Ohio | Vitamin and mineral diets, hormones, enzymes, chemicals. |
| 22. Phipps and Bird, Inc.<br>303 South Sixth Street<br>Richmond 5, Virginia | Kymographs, inductoria, metabolism apparatus, laboratory equipment for biophysics. |
| 23. Quivira Specialties Co.<br>4204 W. 21st Street<br>Topeka, Kansas | Large selection of living and preserved specimens, slides, cages, foods, laboratory equipment. |

* Prefers to sell supplies only to teachers. Turtox Service Leaflets, however, may be purchased by students at three cents per copy. Check the high school library or biology teacher for *Turtox News*.

| COMPANY NAME (alphabetical) | LIST OF SUPPLIES |
| --- | --- |
| 24. Research Scientific Supplies, Inc. Dept. 823 126 West 23rd Street New York 11, New York | Microscopes and slides, living and preserved specimens, fossils, Tyrannosaurus model dinosaur skeletons. |
| 25. Rockland Swiss Mice Rockland Farms New City, New York | Mice. |
| 26. E. H. Sargent and Co. 4647 W. Foster Avenue Chicago 30, Illinois | Chemicals, microscopes, dissecting instruments, blood-pressure apparatus, Tallqvist hemoglobin scales, laboratory equipment. |
| 27. Scientific Products, Division of American Hospital Supply Corp. 1210 Leon Place Evanston, Illinois | Hemolets, blood serums, Tallqvist hemoglobin scales, blood-pressure apparatus, urine analyzers, hemocytometers, surgical equipment, general laboratory equipment. |
| 28. W. C. "Bill" Smith Naturalist P.O. Box 1662 Ocala, Florida | Large selection of snakes, lizards, turtles, crabs, and mammals (mostly from Florida or South America). |
| 29. A. E. Staley Mfg. Co. Rockland Stock Diets Decatur, Illinois | Special feeds for mice, rats, rabbits, guinea pigs, and monkeys. |
| 30. E. G. Steinhilber and Co., Inc. Oshkosh, Wisconsin | Frogs, tadpoles, turtles, clams, crayfish, toads, snails, necturus, worms, mice, rats, pigeons, etc., and preserved specimens. |
| 31. Arthur H. Thomas Company West Washington Square Philadelphia 5, Pennsylvania | General laboratory equipment, chemicals, animal cages, microscopes, clinical apparatus. |
| 32. Ward's Natural Science Establishment, Inc. 3000 Ridge Road East Rochester 9, New York | Living and preserved specimens, microscopes and slides, skeletons, models, charts, animal cages, laboratory equipment. |
| 33. Will Corporation Box 1050 Rochester 3, New York | Laboratory equipment, chemicals, microscopes, slides, preserved materials. |
| 34. Max Wocher and Son, Co. 29–31 West Sixth Street Cincinnati, Ohio | Special apparatus for the physiological laboratory. |

# Appendix F.
## NATIONAL SCIENCE FAIR REGULATIONS FOR EXPERIMENTS WITH ANIMALS

Millions of people visit science fairs each year in the United States. The movement stimulates both the communities and the individuals who participate.

The National Science Fair (sponsored by Science Service, Washington 6, D.C.) has separate divisions for physical and biological sciences. In the latter division they have set up regulations to assure that animals are humanely cared for. The "spirit" of these particular rules should be your guide whether entering competition or not. We give them here verbatim and unabbreviated.

"The basic aim of scientific studies that involve animals is to achieve an understanding of, and a deep respect for, life itself and for all that is living.

"A qualified adult supervisor must assume primary responsibility for the purposes and conditions of any experiment that involves living animals.

"A trained biological scientist, physician, dentist, or veterinarian must directly supervise any experiment that involves anesthetic drugs or surgical procedure.

"Experiments on living animals shall be limited to the use of invertebrates, other non-mammals, and such small mammals as mice, hamsters, guinea pigs, or rabbits. An exception to the above rule is in the case of farm animals, in which case the rules of the local 4-H Club shall be followed. No experiment shall be conducted that involves infection with pathogenic organisms or obviously mutilating surgical procedures, unless the animal is humanely disposed of at the end of the experiment. Any such experiment must be performed with the animal under appropriate anesthesia if pain is involved, and the experiment must be of the briefest possible duration.

"The comfort of the animal used in any study shall be a prime concern of the student investigator. Gentle handling, proper feeding, and provision of appropriate sanitary quarters shall at all times be strictly observed. Any experiment in nutritional deficiency may proceed only to the point where definite symptoms of the deficiency appear. Appropriate measures shall then be taken to correct the deficiency, if such action is feasible. Otherwise, the animal must be humanely disposed of.

"Students shall not be permitted to participate in science fairs held under the auspices of Science Clubs of America until their adult sponsors have submitted assurance in writing that the above rules have been observed."

# INDEX